The Devil's Therapy

Hypnosis Practitioner's Essential
Guide to Effective Regression
Hypnotherapy

Wendie Webber

TribeofHealers.com

The Devil's Therapy: Hypnosis Practitioner's Essential Guide to Effective Regression Hypnotherapy

Wendie Webber

Copyright © 2020 **Wendie Webber**

All Rights Reserved.

First Printing: 2010

ISBN e-book: 978-1-7774121-1-1

ISBN Print Book: 978-1-7774121-0-4

Portions of this book were originally published as The Devil's Therapy: From Hypnosis to Healing e-book.

Wendie Webber

Address: PO Box 55027 SOUTHGATE MALL PO

Nanaimo, British Columbia, Canada

(250)751-5161

www.TribeofHealers.com

For my mother, Olive Webber (1924 – 2019), and my husband, Robert, without whom I never would have been courageous enough to embark on this journey.

WHY READ THIS BOOK

When regression hypnotherapists are asked, "What problem do you struggle with the most in your practice?" the answer is always the same.

Results.

Even though they have all the tools and techniques of regression hypnotherapy, they still struggle with how to consistently get lasting results working with real clients who have real problems.

People don't pay for hypnosis. They pay for results. If you've ever struggled with how to facilitate a healing program . . . or been confused about where to begin . . . or what to do next in a session . . .or doubted your ability to deliver on your promise of results . . . this book is for **you.**

If you're not trained in Regression to Cause hypnotherapy, this isn't the book for you. This is not a "how-to" book on hypnosis. There are no inductions, deepeners, or scripts. We're going beyond hypnosis.

This is no country for the uninitiated.

If you have trained in regression hypnotherapy, this book will change how you think about the healing process of Regression to Cause therapeutic hypnosis. It will help you to better understand the concepts and methods you already have so that you can use them more effectively in your sessions with clients.

Here, the focus is on giving you the theoretical foundation you need to confidently facilitate client-centered healing programs. To get results that last consistently, you need to understand the why of Regression to Cause hypnosis. The Devil's Therapy answers the question *Why we do what we do when we do it?*

Do you want to feel confident guiding the healing process?

Do you want to deliver on your promise of results?

Are you ready to transform your hypnosis sessions into healing sessions?

It's much simpler than you might imagine. The answer lies in the three essential phases of therapeutic hypnosis and a seven-step protocol that can transform your regression hypnosis sessions into healing sessions.

ABOUT

I have never been interested in hypnosis. I don't come from a long line of Mesmerists. It wasn't until I completed my first training in hypnotherapy that I even saw my first stage hypnosis show. I found it pretty boring.

What drew me to hypnosis was a book.

The Healing Power of Illness is about the psychological causes of dis-ease. In it, the author states, "Symptoms are bodily expressions of psychological conflicts, able through their symbolism to reveal the patient's true problems."

I was hooked. I was actually on my fifth reading of the book before it dawned on me it was based on research conducted during regression sessions.

Wait a minute, I said to myself, *regression??? Isn't that hypnosis?* At that moment, it was as if the clouds parted, a choir of angels sang out, and I just knew.

I knew what I wanted to do.

It wasn't *the hypnosis* that interested me, but what you can do with it. Within a few short weeks, I was enrolled in my first hypnosis certification course.

The course promised 160 hours of classroom time and cross-training in multiple disciplines of hypnotherapy. In actuality, the curriculum focused primarily on suggestibility testing, relaxation inductions, and script-reading. There was a heavy emphasis on memorizing useless theory required to pass the written exam. And nothing on regression.

Then, I got my first client.

Sherry had survived a horrible car crash in her teens. Her car had gone off the road late at night and rolled multiple times, ending up in a crumpled mass at the bottom of a ravine. She was lucky to have made it out alive and had to spend months in a hospital recovering.

No one believed Sherry would ever walk again. When she did, she needed a leg brace and cane to support her. The thing is, the doctors said there was nothing medically wrong with her. When Sherry came to me, she was confident that she would walk again.

Sherry had been doing some reading and was convinced that the problem had to do with the trauma of the accident. She was convinced that hypnosis was the answer.

The problem is that I had no idea what to do.

I knew that to resolve traumatic memory required regression hypnosis. But I hadn't been taught that. In fact, in class, we were strongly advised to avoid doing age regression. "Best not to go there!" we were told, "You can do a lot with a good progressive relaxation." Ugh.

My initial excitement of taking on a new client was quickly doused by the grim reality of how ill-prepared I was for the reality of helping real clients and real problems. All I had been taught was relaxation inductions, deepeners, and read them a script. That was not going to get the job done for Sherry.

It seems that my credentials weren't worth the paper on which they were printed. But I knew what to do. Just before graduating from hypnosis school, a group of students had gathered together to watch a video of a professional hypnotist demonstrating an actual hypnotherapy session. This was actually the first time I had ever seen a hypnotherapy session. And I was blown away!

The hypnotist, Gerald Kein, demonstrated an instant induction, tested for somnambulism and regressed the client into a childhood event. And I knew I wanted to do *that* (whatever *that* was). I signed up for the Basic-to-Advanced Hypnotherapy distance training program to learn Regression to Cause therapeutic hypnosis.

And so began a very long journey.

I studied and practiced the Omni-Hypnosis approach to Regression to Cause hypnotherapy for the next nine months. During this time, I enrolled in additional courses, taking introductory counseling courses, an acting class, and hospice training. This gave me the foundation I needed for effective hypnotherapy. But when I found Stephen Parkhill, I knew that I had found what I had been looking for.

Parkhill, a protégé of Gerald Kein, is the author of *Answer Cancer* and creator of Healing with the Mind, a very fast-paced, aggressive approach to healing serious conditions of dis-ease using Regression to Cause hypnosis. When the opportunity arose to attend a live training with Stephen Parkhill, I took the leap. I even volunteered to be the "demo unit" for the class because I wanted to experience regression hypnotherapy from the inside.

This was not what I expected!

The hypnotherapy session started with a powerfully-induced abreaction followed by a breathtakingly rapid, profoundly insightful, emotional roller-coaster ride to the past that resulted in the removal of a breast lump. I kid you not.

This was in 2003, with no recurrence of symptoms since. So, I don't just believe in the power of the Mind to heal. I know. Regression to Cause hypnotherapy is THE WAY to help people heal themselves, their relationships, and their lives.

I continued to learn, studying Alchemical Hypnotherapy, a more spiritual approach to hypnotherapy, which emphasizes Inner Child Work. I took courses in somatic healing and sub-personality work (a.k.a. Ego State or Parts Therapy). Later, I obtained certification in Satir Transformational Systemic Therapy (STST), known as the Satir Method, learning Virginia Satir's approach to Parts Work.

I trained in 5-PATH with Cal Banyan. This is a more clinical approach to regression hypnosis, which taught me to be consistent in my approach. I practiced 5-PATH exclusively for the next two years, during which time I discovered German New Medicine (GNM).

GNM asserts that symptoms are bodily expressions of psychological conflicts, echoing the very thing that brought me into healing hypnosis in the first place — *The Healing Power of Illness.*

GNM's theory of biological conflicts proved very useful in regression sessions by helping me identify the psychological cause of a client's physiological issue. This also helped to solidify one of Parkhill's axiom that "dis-ease is not the body running amok." The body cannot make decisions. Only the Mind can make decisions.

Dis-ease, whether physical, mental, or emotional, is always the result of a life experience. This is where we must look to resolve the problem. This is the basis for Regression to Cause hypnosis. But regression hypnotherapy is not about changing the past. Nor is it about getting rid of the symptoms.

Regression hypnotherapy is about healing the consciousness that *requires* symptoms. The Devil's Therapy is about that.

i.   Thorwald Dethlefsen & Rudiger Dahlke, MD, *The Healing Power of Illness: The Meaning of Symptoms & How to Interpret Them (1997).*

ii.   At that time, 5-PATH stood for 5-Phase Abreactive Regression Therapy, but it has since been changed to be more politically correct.

Stephen Parkhill said, "Anybody can talk about how it's done." Well, that's just what I'm about to do!

WHAT OTHERS SAY

Oh, my goodness . . . how absolutely amazing! I can't stop reading!!

"After failing to get the results I was looking for, I began searching and was feeling so disheartened that I contemplated giving up. I then found this program. It's amazing. Just what I was needing. So much information is included that it has given me the confidence to move forward with my clients, knowing they will experience more through healing." - *Reagan O'Neal, Certified Hypnotherapist, Victoria, B.C.*

A Gift to Regression Hypnotherapists Everywhere

"The Devil's Therapy is a resource to be treasured! Webber's clear, concise, and clever approach helps the practitioner understand how to use regression hypnotherapy to *effectively* heal physical, mental, and emotional trauma at the level of consciousness that produces the symptoms. She fills in knowledge gaps, that all too many hypnotherapists don't receive in their training, from soup to nuts with precision and wit. Webber writes in a lovely, playful, and easy-to-read style as you marvel at the depth of her intellect and openness to share her knowledge. The Devil's Therapy is a gift to regression therapists everywhere and a *must-read* for new hypnotherapists who desire to understand the complete and practical applications for regression to cause." – *Stephanie Conkle, Profound Somnambulism Instructor, Georgia, USA*

Should Be Required Reading in Certification

"Whenever I have hypnosis students or graduates that want to go deeper down the rabbit hole of Regression to Cause, I have always recommended *The Devil's Therapy*. Wendie's in-depth, serious-yet-humourous and personal look at how to affect deep and lasting change should be required reading in certification and advanced hypnotherapy training courses." - *Beryl Comar. Emotional Intelligence Development Specialist, Author: HypnoDontics*

Shines a Bright Light on Hypnosis, Healing & Regression

Wendie delivers her work with enthusiasm, passion and, above all, a deep knowledge and love for the subject of healing. Her compassion and kindness know no bounds. She is a fountain of knowledge and expertise in many areas. A remarkable lady who shines a bright light on the phenomenal world of Hypnosis, Healing & Regression. The best in her field! - *Jacquelyn Haley, JSH Hypnosis, Wales, UK*

A Delight!

"The Devil's Therapy is a delight! The story captured and kept my attention throughout the entire book. I appreciated the smooth transition into the lessons I found to be fascinating. I was able to utilize all the techniques, for they made complete sense to me. I recommend this book to anyone who wants knowledge that can be applied to their therapy or just for a very enjoyable and interesting read." - *Paul Challenger Hypnotherapy, Grand Cayman, Cayman Islands*

The Perfect Tool to Get the Greatest Outcomes

Wendie is the one of the most outstanding Regression to Cause teachers out there. Her understanding of how to get great results with R2C is second to none. This book contains all her wisdom and understanding of the subject and is the perfect tool for people who want to be able to get the greatest outcomes with their clients. - *Ines Simpson, The Simpson Protocol, SimpsonProtocol.com*

Take a Walk on the Wild Side

Guys - we all know Regression to Cause is the Porsche in hypnotherapy. Well, get ready to drive the Porsche in the Convertible Version - with Wendie Webber. Turn up the music in the radio - Lou Reed's playing "Take a walk on the wild side," and get ready to be fined…. You might be exceeding the speed limit! Rock n' Roll, the devil is sitting in your passenger's seat! Yeah! Enjoy the ride! - *Barbara Scholl, OMNI HypnoKids® Instructor, Zurich Switzerland.*

A Fresh Look at Hypnotherapy

The Devil's Therapy is the first fresh look at hypnotherapy I have read in years. Her down-to-earth style - "People don't pay for hypnosis. They pay for results"- along with her theoretical foundation, allowing us to get consistent results, make this a book a 'MUST add' to my library of important books by trained thought providers and thought leaders. I recommend this book to anyone interested in learning about our minds and how they work. - *Bunny Vreeland, Ph.D,. Upgrade Your Life With Dr. Bunny, Clinical Hypnotherapist, Coach, Author, California, USA*

A Leading Resource Book for the Serious Practitioner

"The Devil's Therapy is a highly impressive body of work that will undoubtedly benefit every Regression-to-Cause Hypnotist, on every level of experience. Wendie Webber, in her delightfully captivating manor, shares her vast knowledge of the power of the mind and using hypnosis for the purpose of emotional, behavioral, and physical healing. A leading resource book for the serious practitioner. - *Helga Rahn, Inner Harmony Hypnosis, Rochester, NY, USA*

A Must-Have for the Modern Therapist

"Not only is it a good resource for beginners, showing how to get set up and what to do to get known, but also for experienced and advanced therapists who are looking for 'something' to help with 'that awkward client.' Wendie has enormous experience, and this manual sits well in my bookcase for the 'when' I need it." - *Piers Day, Certified Professional Hypnosis Instructor, Suffolk, UK*

A Remarkable Synthesis of the Best Techniques in Hypnosis

"*The Devil's Therapy* is a remarkable synthesis of the best techniques in hypnosis —featuring numerous instructive anecdotes gathered everywhere from myth to pop culture. An essential read for the contemporary hypnotherapist." - *Spencer Todd, Coquitlam, BC*

Leaves No Doubt About What to Do

"This is absolutely amazing work. It's so clear and precise, just like a laser. It leaves no doubts about what to do, how to do it, and the best part: Why to do it!!" - *Zoran Pavlovic, Belgrade, Serbia*

TABLE OF CONTENTS

FOREWORD

As a retired octogenarian, I thought that after nearly 60 years of practice and research in the field of hypnotherapy, I had already read everything of value and a great deal of much, which was not. During this time, it was my privilege to be one of the few accredited examiners in the subject. As such, it was incumbent upon me to find flaws in the argument and fact in each of the papers presented to me and marked down accordingly. It is with this background and this bias that I read Wendie Webber's *The Devils Therapy*.

It is not in my nature to give high marks indiscriminately, but to me, this book would have to deserve a high distinction in every aspect of its delivery. Wendie has shown an insightful and scholarly approach to hypnotherapy that I have found exceeds anything I have yet come across. Add to that a highly readable narrative and explanation of every step of the way through this masterpiece makes it very difficult to pause even for a cup of tea or coffee.

The history of hypnotherapy has often been written about, but her chronological discourse on the history has been expertly tackled by this writer. Her sequencing and historical research are impeccable. I was also aware of the illustrations and metaphors used being highly relevant to the text and backing up the written word to make the issues referred to doubly memorial.

Throughout the book, in each chapter, every aspect of the reasoning is backed up by logic and illustrated by metaphor in such an enlightened manner to hold the reader's interest throughout the whole book.

Entertaining and inspiring to read like a novel as well as an authoritative backup for anyone either in the field or aspiring to enter it. In addition to her own specialties, she gives a concise and thorough description of all those therapies that bear on the main subject of hypnotherapy.

It is rare in my experience to find so many qualities, all combined with superior intelligence and native intuition. This is a book that I would regard as a *must-read* for any therapist in any discipline within the rubric of the helping professions and a quality read for the general public.

Bryan J Perry (Dip Hyp SA) (Grad Dip Health Ed)

CHAPTER 1:
Why the Devil?

Historically, anything that runs counter to culturally accepted values and thinking has been deemed the work of *the devil*. Take bloodletting, for example. At one time, bloodletting was the accepted preventative and medical treatment. Natural healers, who refused to perform this treatment, were accused of doing the work of the devil. The lay practitioners who took care of births, illness, and injury through the use of herbs and folk medicine were tortured and slaughtered for their evil doing.

Today we have chemical therapies. Body and mind are viewed as separate and treated accordingly. Any natural approach to healing is considered unscientific and, therefore, suspect. This includes hypnosis. Hypnotherapy is still considered somewhat counter-culture. After all, it's not bloodletting; it's not chemical therapy. It's an approach to self-healing that requires going within and working *with* the Subconscious Mind.

If there is a hell, this is it.

Hell is within. It's *the shadow,* the territory of the Subconscious Mind where all our instinctive and primitive drives for self-preservation and procreation exist. This is a place of seemingly irrational feelings and instinctual energies like passion, rage, and the four Fs of fight, flee, feed, and fornicate.

When we repress a part of ourselves, it does not go away. It goes underground. When we deny, reject, judge, or condemn any Part of ourselves, it is relegated to the *shadow*. From there, it can wreak havoc – physically, mentally, emotionally, and spiritually – by enslaving us with inhibitions or drives to excess. Until reclaimed, these disowned energies are trapped inside, making the Mind a living hell.

This is the hell. - **Stephen Parkhill**

The devil represents everything that runs contrary to the ways of the world. Anything judged unacceptable must be denied, or rejected, and sent straight to hell. If you wish to be freed of uncomfortable feelings and unconscious drives or impulses, you must go to the devil because the Subconscious Mind is his domain.

The devil, you say?

The word devil actually grew out of the same root word for divinity (devi/deva). The most ancient teachings tell us that originally there were twin gods. One ruled over heaven, the other ruled over the earth. Like yin and yang, the twins work in partnership. They're not really separate. One heads up the corporate office – the other works in the field. Managing creation is a big job, after all. This division of duties is at least practical.

The ancients believed that, in order to get what you wanted, you needed to petition the correct god. If you wanted the things of heaven – intangibles like peace, love, joy, gratitude – you had to go upstairs. If you wanted material stuff — gold, success on the battlefield, fame, worldly knowledge, physical healing, a new ass — you went to the devil.

Traditionally, the devil is responsible for the material world. All the stuff of our earthly, physical existence — including the body - is the domain of the devil.

The Problem with Good & Evil

The origin of the devil, as we know it today, can be found in the monotheistic Hebrew cult of YHVH (Yahweh). Originally, they had a pantheon of gods and goddesses known as Elohim. There was a god for everything. Downsizing to a single god certainly helped simplify things. But the one all-powerful, all-good god idea created a logistical problem.

The fact that all life is pain and suffering didn't escape the early Hebrews. An all-powerful God could surely make life *without* all the hurt and pain and suffering. If he *wouldn't*, then logically, he couldn't be all good. If he *wanted* to make a world free of pain and suffering, and *could not*, then logically, he couldn't be all-powerful.

The solution was to put a new spin on the twin gods. Keep the all-powerful, all-good god and make the other one a little sh*t-disturber on which to hang the blame! And so, the devil, a.k.a. Satan, came into being. This practice of scapegoating likely has its roots in ancient Syrian custom where, on the occasion of the king's wedding, a she-goat would be driven out into the wasteland of Alini, ritualistically cleansing the community by carrying away evils (not sins).

While this solution of having a scapegoat worked for the Yahwists, it created a new problem. Good and evil are not separate. They are relevant terms; two sides of the same coin. Separating good and evil creates a conflict in the mind! That's hell.

Pleased to meet you, hope you guessed my name . . . - **Rolling Stones**

The word satan means adversary or opponent or enemy. It's something or someone we resist. Externally, it might take the form of a foe, a rival tribe, and their heathen god. Internally, it might take shape as anxiety or lust driving an unwanted (sinful) behavior like excessive smoking, eating, gambling, drinking, sexing, etc. Sound familiar?

What makes anything evil is a matter of perception. If something or someone is perceived to be a source of adversity, what tends to follow is resistance. Whether it's a neighboring tribe or an uncomfortable feeling, the tendency is to try to get rid of it. This is the basis of war.

Interestingly, in Matthew 39, the Bible counsels, "Resist not evil." Carl Jung echoed this wisdom when he wrote, "What I resist, persists."

Light & Darkness

The early Egyptians, faced with the incomprehensible nature of the Divine, came up with a pantheon of gods as symbolic representations of the many attributes of the Godhead. Set (or Seth, Setan, or Seteh), was the Egyptian equivalent of the devil who, by the way, also had a brother-god. Set was the god of the desert, storms, darkness, and chaos. If you wanted power over the forces of chaos and darkness, you called upon Set.

One of the oldest Egyptian gods was the sun god, Ra, who called forth all forms of life by uttering their secret names. This belief is echoed in the creation myths of both the Kabbalists and Australian Aboriginals. Ra was the source of light and giver of life. When you died, you went back into the light. You fed on and were nourished by light. And you became one with the light.

Clearly, there's nothing new about the New Age. But over time, Egyptians became more materialistic and literal in their thinking. The gods began to be viewed as independent deities that could be bargained with to attain one's desired ends. The *riches in heaven* one could expect following death changed from supernatural light to actual stuff. Now, you could take it with you. Preparing for death became a very important part of everyday life.

There were many temples and sanctuaries in Egypt, each one dedicated to a different god. After all, if you wanted the job done right, you needed to contract the appropriate god. And business was booming for those who served up the gods to the public.

When Amenhotep IV took the throne in 1380 BC, he changed his name to Akhenaten (in honor of the sun god, Aten, whom he equated with Ra) and promptly set to work on social reforms which included doing away with polytheism. As might be expected, Akhenaten's attempts to return Egypt to monotheism met with strong resistance.

And he soon earned himself the reputation of a heretic king.

When his plans to restructure society failed, Akhenaten lead his loyal followers out into the desert to worship the one true god in peace. Interestingly, Freud theorized that Akhenaten and the biblical Prince of Egypt, Moses, were one and the same historical character.

After building a city in the desert where the faithful could worship Aten, Akhenaten ruled for another 17 years. After his death, sometime around 1336 BC, all evidence of his existence was erased, including his city. And the culturally accepted shrines and temples of many gods continued to thrive and prosper.

Good Greek!

The Greeks loved everything Egyptian. Alexander (The Very Good) brought home many customs and practices to Greece, including sleep temples. These healing temples provided a setting in which sufferers of various ailments could practice rituals and purification rites before entering into an induced *sleep*.

The ancient Greeks also practiced scapegoating by selecting a cripple, beggar, or criminal, called pharmakos, who would be cast out of the community in response to some crisis or natural disaster. It is interesting to note that the term pharmakos later became the term *pharmakeus*, which refers to "a drug, spell-giving potion, druggist, poisoner, and by extension, a magician or a sorcerer. A variation of this term is "pharmakon," a complex term meaning sacrament, remedy, poison, talisman, cosmetic, perfume or intoxicant. From this, the modern term "pharmacology" emerged.

The Greeks took healing very seriously and kept good records. Archeologists discovered in the ruins of the Temple of Epidaurus over 100,000 documented healings. It's no surprise that sleep temples gained in popularity and were soon adopted by the Romans and, later, the early Christians. Then, around the year 1000 AD, church reform brought these healing practices into disrepute. As the church gained power, it became heretical to seek direct contact with the Divine. What had once been good was now *evil*.

It's Science!

During the middle ages (when the earth was still flat and logging practices hadn't yet been invented), people lived in small communities that were separated by vast wooded areas. There were always men or women who lived alone at the forest's edge, usually midwives and healers. Living close to nature allowed them to gather their remedies for healing and stay clear of the local riff-raff.

When needed, these healing practitioners were sought out but, otherwise, were of little concern to the villagers. That is until the Inquisition came to town.

The Inquisitors were professionals. Many were medical practitioners whose motive was to promote rationalized scientific medicine. They quickly accused the old ways as heretical. As a result, popular healers were especially targeted for prosecution, and bonfire season began. Holding views contrary to church doctrine soon became a life-threatening condition!

When Astronomer Copernicus (1473 – 1543) theorized that the sun, and not the earth, was at the center of the universe, he kept his views to himself. Being branded a heretic would bring his family into disrepute and could end in imprisonment or even death. It was not until he was on his deathbed that he dared to publish his heretical views.

By the late 1700s, a German physician named Franz Mesmer began developing a new form of healing called *animal magnetism*. As stories of miracles spread, Mesmer came under the scrutiny of the established medical (bloodletting) profession. And before long, Mesmer's heretical practices were disavowed. Science, it seems, was the new *good*.

Mesmerized

Fortunately, Mesmerism survived and eventually made its way to America. Sometime around 1836, a French mesmerist named Charles Poyen was giving a lecture in Belfast, Maine. Phineas Parkhurst Quimby, a watchmaker, was so impressed by Poyen that he quit his job to become a Mesmerist and became the best-known mental healer in America.

Around the same time as Quimby, Scottish neurosurgeon James Braid had begun experimenting on his own methods based on Mesmerism. Braid was attempting to develop a more scientific approach, which he called rational mesmerism and then later neuro-hypnotism (from Hypnos, the Greek god of sleep).

Braid later attempted to change the name to emphasize more accurately the concept of *mental concentration on a single idea*, but the term monoideism never caught on. When Braid came under personal attack from the clergy for satanic agency, hypnotism went the way of the devil.

In America, in a proper scientific manner, Quimby carefully documented his opinions, beliefs, and techniques over a 15-year period. Unfortunately, he loaned his manuscripts to an ex-patient, Mary Patterson (who later became Mary Baker, then Mary Baker Edy), who did not return them (perhaps because she was too busy getting married and founding the Christian Science Church).

It was not until 1921, 55 years after his death, that the manuscripts eventually made their way back to Quimby's family. Quimby theorized that patients possess the power to heal themselves, provided they have both the motivation and the means. He further theorized that 70% of all diseases are caused by wrong beliefs.

He practiced a silent healing technique where he would feel the patient's disease, create an image to represent it, change the image, and *send it back*. Quimby is credited with healing over a thousand people during this period.

> *What good is a belief if it does not benefit your life?* - **Phineas Parkhurst Quimby, 1862**

Meanwhile, the church which had been founded upon Quimby's healing principles now denied hypnosis. What had once been good now went the way of Mesmer's animal magnetism, the Egyptian and Greek sleep temples, and the pantheon of gods – straight onto Freud's couch.

Psychotherapy

Neurologist Sigmund Freud (1856 – 1939) studied with Europe's most renowned neurologist, Jean-Martin Charcot, who specialized in the study of hysteria and hypnosis suggestibility. Freud's use of hypnosis, however, was for the purpose of locating and releasing powerful emotional energy that had been repressed.

Repression is defined as "subconscious rejection of thoughts and impulses that conflict with conventional standards of conduct." Psychologist, Carl Jung, a student of Freud, theorized that conflicting ideas, desires, and emotions cause us to lose touch with our core self, separating us from the awareness of our primal integrity. By unconsciously repressing, suppressing, and disowning parts of ourselves, we can disconnect from our self energetically.

The aspects of ourselves that we have denied, rejected, and judged are then sentenced to hell. Once relegated to the shadow, they will wreak havoc in our lives until reclaimed.

This disconnection in Mind is actually at the root of every problem. It is this collective idea of separateness that Jung viewed as the devil.

Psychobiology

Hippocrates (*ca.* 460 BC – ca. 370 BC) is considered the father of modern medicine. He observed that the body is intelligent and has all the information it needs to heal itself. Hippocrates called this the healing power of nature.

Mesmer (1734 – 1815) called this power animal magnetism. But long before Mesmer or Hippocrates, the physicians of China studied the movement of qi or ch'i through the body's energy system of meridians (1700 BCE).

The ayurvedic doctors of India (1500 BCE) worked with a system of chakras, wheel-shaped energy centers that correspond with major nerve plexuses located along the spinal column. These nerve plexuses serve to either transmit sensory messages to the Central Nervous System (CNS) or carry motor impulses away from the CNS to the tissues, e.g., muscles.

While it remains a mystery as to how this healing power works, exactly, one thing is certain –stress blocks its natural flow. The American Institute of Stress estimates that between 75% and 90% of all visits to primary healthcare providers are for stress-related complaints.

These conditions include problems with:

- Anxiety

- Sleep

- Health

- Weight

- Intestinal

- Skin

- Confidence

- Self-worth

- Relationship

- Habitual behavioral and more.

Stress disrupts our sleep. It inhibits our ability to think clearly and perform well. And, most bad habits started as a way of coping with stress. Sleep problems, weight problems, intestinal problems like irritable bowel syndrome (IBS) and gastroesophageal reflux disease GERD, skin problems such as eczema and psoriasis, and a myriad of other chronic conditions have their roots in stress.

Stress is recognized to inhibit immune function contributing to allergies, asthma, rheumatism, and even cancer. Current research is exploring the stress connection with Alzheimer's disease. But what is stress? For our purposes, stress is simply the body's natural response to any perceived threat, real or imagined.

The body's nervous system is designed to keep us alive, so when danger is perceived, either consciously or unconsciously, the nervous system goes on red alert. When that happens, stress hormones are released into the bloodstream to prepare the body for emergency action. Hormones like cortisol and adrenaline flood the system, making the heart beat faster, muscles tighten, blood pressure rises, and breathing quickens. All senses get sharper.

Once the threat is gone, the body discharges these hormones from the system and returns to a normal state of rest and relaxation. But while under the influence of these stress hormones, we're more focused, our reaction time is quicker, and we have increased strength and stamina, which is especially useful if you happen to be facing a saber-toothed tiger! What's not good is chronic stress.

Modern living has left us feeling overwhelmed. While we rarely encounter actual predators or threats to our lives, we have chronic stressors that trigger the body's fight-flight response. We have too much to do and not enough time to do it. We are assaulted by too much information. We have too many responsibilities. We're dealing with arguments with the spouse, kids, the boss, not enough money, too much bureaucracy, social media, etc.

Maude, a cartoon character of *The Simpsons,* wryly suggests, "Most stress is caused by three things: Money, family, and family with no money." It's funny because, too often, it's true. The problem is that the body does not know the difference between a real and psychological threat. It responds to our perception of a threat as if it was a life-or-death situation.

These chronic stressors keep the body on red alert, continually flooding it with stress hormones that disrupt every system in the body. They suppress immune function and slow healing. They make inflammatory problems worse, increasing muscle and joint pain. They contribute to insomnia and fatigue, literally wears us out, and aging us before our time.

Excess cortisol actually kills brain cells resulting in mental haziness, forgetfulness, and confusion. Cortisol affects the metabolic function, which regulates blood sugar. Have you ever had a carb-craving? Another stress-related hormone, Norepinephrine, is believed to play a role in attention-deficit hyperactivity disorder (ADHD), depression, and hypertension.

Dr. Gerd Hamer of The German New Medicine (GNM) says that "the origin of disease is a life experience." He believes that symptoms of disease serve a biological purpose of survival. Any experience, whether real or symbolic that is perceived as threatening in some way will register as a lesion on the brain. The organs controlled by that part of the brain will then begin to express as symptoms.

This suggests that everything, even physical disease, begins with a perception in the mind. Change the perception, and the body will follow. The physical behavior or emotional response will then self-correct according to Nature's own self-healing system, just as Hippocrates observed.

It's clear that, as a species, we are programmed to survive. Our biological programming at birth contains basic instincts, stress responses, and the ability to learn from our experiences. But our psychological well-being has much to do with experiences growing up. The way we were treated as children and the messages we received from the people around us – parents, teachers, and other people in authority – shaped how we think, feel, and behave as adults.

In the late 1800s, leading experts advised parents and caregivers not to spoil children by picking them up when they cried or handling them too much. As a result, children were fed by the clock rather than on demand. When these methods were applied in institutions, however, children's mortality rate under the age of one was often as high as 100%. Why did these babies expire? After all, their physical needs were being provided. They were adequately fed and kept clean and warm.

What went wrong?

What science failed to recognize is that our most basic human need is for love. Human beings take in information through the five senses. We see, hear, smell, taste, and touch aspects of our environment. The sensory system of the body is developed by seven weeks in-utero. From conception until about six years of age, we download massive amounts of information from our environment. If the things that are said or done to us as children are perceived as loving, they will generate feelings of comfort and well-being. If they are perceived as unloving, they will generate a stress response.

Mind and body do not function independently. All feelings are the energy of the nervous system. We feel this energy as sensations and emotions in the body. Our language reflects this. We describe the feeling of disappointment as a sinking heart. When we feel nervous, we describe butterflies in our stomachs. Depression feels like a heavy weight on the chest, while joy is experienced as a physical lightness and sense of freedom.

Candace Pert, the best-selling author of *Molecules of Emotion*,[6] says, "Your body is your Subconscious Mind." The Subconscious Mind holds onto all your memories. Memories are experiences that made an impression on the nervous system of the body. The body remembers so that you will know how to respond in the future.

When we're young, we don't have the knowledge-base from which to judge what's happening 100% of the time accurately. Many of our perceptions as children were simply inaccurate. Events that, to Adult consciousness might seem insignificant, can feel overwhelming to a small child.

In the absence of critical thinking, these perceptions are not checked for accuracy. They are simply accepted as truths that form the foundation for the belief system. Our belief system then tells us who we are, how relationships work, whether the world is a safe or dangerous place, and what to expect in the future. From this, we know whether life is about flow or struggle, abundance, or scarcity.

The devil made me do it.

Regression to Cause therapeutic hypnosis is about healing with the Mind. The Mind is non-physical and is concerned with consciousness. Consciousness refers to the ability to be aware of your existence. It is self-awareness, which includes perceptions, thoughts, feelings, and actions/reactions/behaviors. That's where we work!

The word heal comes from the Old English, meaning to make whole. The goal is nothing less than a complete resolution of the client's issue. As most problems that we work with are the result of repression, suppression, denial, and rejection of Parts of the self, the solution lies in recognizing, accepting, reclaiming, and re-integrating these Parts. It is through this lens that we will view the process of healing with Regression to Cause hypnosis.

As for the devil – I get it. Some people aren't comfortable with the title of this book. It triggers uncomfortable feelings and emotions based on unquestioned beliefs. That's because, culturally, the devil is taboo. But you can relax. If you've read this far, prepare for an interesting journey because the real reason I called it the Devil's Therapy is because I used a Grimm's Fairy Tale to illustrate the entire healing process of regression hypnotherapy.

Stephen Parkhill, the author of *Answer* Cancer, once said, "Anybody can talk about how it's done." Well, that's what I'm going to do.

Through the story of *The Devil's Grimy Brother*, you will discover:

- The 3 Essential Phases to Achieving Lasting Results

- A 7-Phase Protocol for Regression-to-Cause Hypnotherapy

- The 4 Universal Healing Steps

- and much, much more.

In Phase 1, you will learn how the secret to successful Regression to Cause therapeutic hypnosis is in your set-up. You'll learn:

- How to Establish the Therapeutic Relationship

- Preliminary Uncovering Techniques

- How to Identify the Symptom Resolution Keys

- How to Establish the Therapeutic Contract

- How to Test and Prepare the Client for Regression to Cause Hypnosis

- How to Make the Client Responsible for the Results

In Phase 2, you will learn how to facilitate the transformational process of regression hypnotherapy. You'll learn:

- How to Locate the Underlying Cause

- A Developmental Mind Model

- 3 Key Events in Regression to Cause Hypnosis

- How to Find a Bridge to the Past

- How to Test for the Causal Event

- How to Uncover the Real Cause of the Problem

- Inner Child Work.

In Phase 3, you will learn the key to consistently achieving lasting results. You'll learn:

- How to Test and Integrate Change

- How to Test to Ensure the Causal Event is Clear

- How to Test and Compound All Changes

- The Only True Test of the Results

- The Secret to Forgiveness Work

- The Forgiveness Test

- and much more.

Let's get started!

i.   I make a distinction between a hypnotist and hypnotherapist. For our purposes, hypnotist refers to anyone who practices hypnotism. Hypnotherapist refers to the use of hypnotism for the purposes of healing using age regression and other therapeutic methods.

ii.   Source: Wikipedia.

iii.   Freud is considered the father of psychoanalysis.

iv.   www.thefreedictionary.com

v.   www.germannewmedicine.ca

vi.   Candace Pert, *Molecules of Emotions: The Science Behind Mind Body Medicine (1999).*

vii.   Candace Pert, *Your Body is Your Subconscious Mind, Audio CD (2004).*

CHAPTER 2:
A Grimm's Fairy Tale: The Devil's Grimy Brother

A discharged soldier had no money left and didn't know where to turn. So, he went out into the forest. And after a while, he met a little man. This little man was the devil.

The devil asked the soldier, "What ails you? You look so unhappy."

The soldier answered, "I'm hungry, and I haven't any money."

The Devil said, "If you'll hire yourself out to me and be my serving-man, you shall have enough to last you the rest of your life. But there are some conditions. You'll have to serve me for seven years, and after that, you'll be free.

"But," said the Devil, "one thing I must tell you, and that is, during those seven years you must not wash, or comb, or cut your hair, or trim your beard, or pare your nails, or wipe the water from your eyes."

The soldier replied, "If it can't be helped, I may as well get started." So, off he went with the little man, who led him straight to hell. There, the devil told him what to do –tend the fires under the caldrons where the damned souls are cooking; clean the house; carry the sweepings behind the back door, and, in general, keep order.

"But," said the Devil, "don't look into those caldrons! Not even once, or you'll be in trouble." The soldier said that he understood and promised everything would be all right. And the devil went off on his travels, leaving the soldier to take up his duties tending the fire, sweeping, carrying the sweepings behind the back door – everything just as he'd been instructed.

When the devil came back to see that his man had done his work, said, "Well done," and went away again.

This time the soldier took a good look around, and in every corner of hell, the caldrons were boiling and bubbling, with furious fires under them. He'd have loved to look into them, but the devil had expressly forbidden it.

At last, he could no longer restrain himself. The temptation became too much, and he lifted the lid off the first caldron, just a little, and peeked inside. And what did he discover but his old sergeant. "Aha, you dog!" he said, "You here? You made it hot for me! Now I'll make it hot for you." Whereupon, he dropped the lid, stirred up the fire, and put on some more wood.

Next, he went to the second caldron, lifted the lid a little, and looked in. This one had his lieutenant inside. "Aha, you dog!" he said, "You here? You made it hot for me! Now I'll make it hot for you." He closed the lid again and fetched yet another log to make it really hot.

Then, he wanted to see who might be shut up in the third kettle. It was actually a general! "Aha, you dog!" he said, "You here? You made it hot for me! Now I'll make it hot for you." And he fetched the bellows and made hell-fire flare well up under him.

And so, he went on to perform his duties in hell for seven years. He didn't wash, he didn't comb or cut his hair, or pare his nails, or wipe his eyes. And the seven years passed so quickly it seemed as if he hadn't been there for more than half a year.

When his time was finally up, the devil returned and said, "Well, Hans, what have you done all this time?" And Hans gave him a report, "Well, I've tended the fires under the caldrons, swept up and carried the sweepings behind the door."

"But," said the devil, "you also looked into the caldrons! Good thing you put on more wood or you'd have lost your life. Well, it looks like your time is up. Do you want to go back home?"

"Oh, yes," said the soldier. "I should very much like to see what my father is doing at home." "You've earned your reward," said the Devil. "Here's how to get it. Go behind the door and fill your knapsack with sweepings, and take them home with you.

"Oh, and you must also go unwashed and uncombed, with long hair and a long beard, with uncut nails and bleary eyes. And if anyone asks you where you've come from, you must say, 'from hell.' And if they ask you who you are, you must say, 'The devil's grimy brother and my king as well!'"

The soldier held his peace and did as the devil had instructed without complaint, but he wasn't at all pleased with his reward.

As soon as he was back in the woods, again, he took his knapsack off his back to empty it. He was actually going to throw the sweepings away, but when he opened the pack, he discovered the sweepings had turned to pure gold. "Wow! This is a pleasant surprise," he said to himself and was well-pleased.

He then proceeded to the nearest town, where an innkeeper was standing in the doorway of his inn. When the innkeeper saw Hans coming along, he was frightened to death because Hans looked awful, worse than a scarecrow. "Where have you come from?" he asked. "From hell," replied Hans. "Who are you?" asked the innkeeper. "The devil's grimy brother, and my king as well," replied Hans.

The innkeeper didn't want to let him enter, but when Hans showed him his gold, the innkeeper unlatched the door himself. Hans ordered the best room and the finest service and proceeded to eat and drink his fill. He adhered to the devil's instructions and didn't wash or comb his hair. And finally, he lay down to sleep.

All this time, the innkeeper hadn't been able to get that full bag of gold out of his mind. The thought of it gave him no peace. So finally, late that night, he crept in and stole it.

When Hans got up the next morning and prepared to pay the innkeeper so he could leave, he realized his knapsack was gone. He thought to himself, *I'm in trouble through no fault of my own* and straightway decided what to do.

He retraced his steps, going straight back to hell, where he told the devil his tale of woe and asked for help. The devil said, "Sit down. I'll wash you. I'll comb and cut your hair. I'll trim your nails and wipe your eyes."

When the devil was finished, he gave Hans back his backpack full of sweepings and said, "Now go and tell the innkeeper to give you back your gold. Tell him, if he doesn't, he'll end up tending the fires in your place."

Hans did as he was instructed. He went up to the Innkeeper and said, "You stole my money. If you don't give it back, you'll go to hell in my place. And you'll look every bit as horrible as I did."

Not only did the innkeeper give Hans back his money, but some more besides, begging Hans to keep it a secret and not to tell anybody. So, now Hans was a rich man.

He started on the way home to his father and bought himself a coarse white coat. As he went on his way, he played music, for he had learned how to do that from the devil in hell.

There was, however, an old king in that country, before whom he had to play. The king was so delighted with his playing that he promised Hans, his eldest daughter in marriage.

But when the daughter heard that she was to be married to a lowborn fellow in a coarse white coat, she declared, "Before I do that, I'll jump into the deepest river." So, the king gave Hans his youngest daughter, who was willing to do it to please her father.

A big wedding followed. And thus, the devil's grimy brother got the king's daughter. And when the old king died, Hans became king over the whole country.

What's this got to do with hypnosis?

Read on.

PHASE 1: SET-UP

Set-Up Phase		
1 INTAKE	2 EDUCATE	3 TEST
Establish Therapeutic Relationship	*Establish Therapeutic Contract*	*Test & Prepare for R2C*
1.1 Preliminary Uncovering	2.1 Hypnosis Agreement	3.1 Hypnosis Tests
1.2 Identify Symptom Resolution Keys	2.2 Regression Agreement	3.2 Regression Tests
		3.3 Teach Universal Healing

When you discover what people will spend on having their nails or hair done, you will see that it is not about the money but the perceived value. Often, this money issue will be the first thing the client wants to talk about . . . this is often a sign that, while they wish to have the benefit, they don't actually wish to spend any money to achieve that (and thus subtly devalue you and the therapy! The genuine clients will make the effort. — **Dr. David Lake, EFT Downunder**

CHAPTER 3:
Success is in Your Set Up

A discharged soldier had no money left and didn't know where to turn. So, he went out into the forest. And after a while, he met a little man. This little man was the devil.

Our early conditioning in the world is like a military boot camp! Like a family system, the army provides a sense of belonging and security. It has clearly-defined roles and responsibilities. There's a hierarchy with parental-authorities who make all the decisions.

Every child learns to obey their commanding officers/parents. Good behavior is rewarded with medals and promotions. Bad behavior is punished with demerits or the brig. We learned long ago to give up our own rhythm and march to the beat of society's drum by repressing impulses, thoughts, wishes, fantasies, and feelings and assume the culturally approved attitude. We've been trained to be tough little soldiers, as were those who taught us and those before them.

War is hell. - **Iain Overton**

The Tough Little Soldier

Every client who comes to you is like a discharged soldier. They have survived a war. After all, what is war if not a state of conflict? For many, the war may be over, but the conflict continues. And like our hero, they are condemned to wander through life, feeling lost and powerless, not knowing where to turn. Maybe the client lost their job. Perhaps they've been through a divorce or have been diagnosed with an illness. They've been discharged from their old, familiar role in the pecking order. That's an identity issue.

A tough little soldier is a good little repressive, well-prepared for the battlefield of life. They know that questioning the rules can bring dire consequences. They know how to suck it up and not wimp-out when it hurts. They know how to survive. But it comes at a cost to their happiness by disconnecting them from their innermost feelings of goodness and worth. In Stanley Kubrick's abrasive movie, Full Metal Jacket, Gunnery Sergeant Hartman barks, "What is your major malfunction, numb-nuts? Didn't Mommy and Daddy show you enough attention when you were a child?"

This is the human condition. Here we are, eternal souls on planet earth, and what are our earliest lessons? Gunnery Sergeant Hartman put it this way, "You are the lowest form of life on Earth. You are not even human-fucking beings. You are nothing but unorganized, grabastic pieces of amphibian shit. There is no racial bigotry here. I do not look down on niggers, kikes, wops, or greasers. Here, you are all equally worthless."

While the circumstances in life may have precipitated symptoms, the problem is never just the symptoms. Often, the real problem is rooted in trauma. Post-traumatic stress disorder (PTSD) is a common condition among veterans and homeless people alike. But post-traumatic stress is not reserved solely for the battlefield. Too often, it's a condition of childhood.

This is what the Devil's Therapy is really about – healing the Inner Child the healing process; the soldier will learn how to grow themselves up so that, as an adult, they can embody their true nature. This will take some time, though. Healing is, after all, a process. It won't be until the devil finally calls the soldier Hans that the transformation will have occurred.

The Guy in the Woods

Back in the 1990s, Jim Henson produced a TV show called Dinosaurs. The program was liberally sprinkled with social commentary and was highly entertaining. In one episode, the baby dinosaur comes down with something and is very sick. And the crotchety old grandmother, who lives with the dinosaur family, advises the parents to take the child to *the Guy in the Woods.*

Daddy dinosaur states clearly that he will not listen to grandma's antiquated ideas, insisting that baby be taken to a real doctor. Off they go with the baby to see the medical doctor who prescribes an expensive modern drug.

When that fails, another is prescribed. And then another. With each more potent remedy, the baby gets worse. Meanwhile, grandma is starting to sound like a scratchy old record stuck on, "Go to the Guy in the Woods!"

It's not until the bank account has been drained, and a second mortgage was taken out on the family home that daddy dinosaur admits the miracles of modern science might not be the answer. Off they go to the Guy in the Woods, who takes one look at the baby and says, "Give him some moldy bread!"

Daddy dinosaur is incensed! "MOLDY BREAD?!" But he's broke, and nobody has any better ideas, so he agrees to give it a try. And naturally, baby dinosaur recovers, thanks to the fringe-dwelling Guy in the Woods.

Like the devil, you're not viewed by society as a big man. You don't have big, impressive credentials or wear a white lab coat. You're not a doctor or a lawyer. You're just an ordinary guy or gal who, to some folks, seems a bit *out there*. Some people may even accuse you of doing the work of the devil. It's not their fault. We have all been socially conditioned to avoid uncomfortable feelings and emotions. Got a headache? Take a pill. Got anxiety? Put it inside a box and bury it. The problem with conventional approaches is that they only treat the symptoms.

The devil does not adhere to conventional thinking and methodologies. His medicine is the healing power of nature. And in our increasing socialization, we have cast out aspects of our human nature. But the devil isn't merely the Guy in the Woods. He is also known as Pan, the great spirit of Nature. His remedies are simple and practical. They don't fix the problem. They restore the patient to his own nature and, in so doing, re-establish balance. That's when healing happens.

Hippocrates, the father of modern medicine, taught his medical students some pretty devilish concepts. Hippocrates believed that the body knows how to heal itself. He taught that the source of all healing is an invisible energy he called *vis medicatrix naturae* (the healing power of nature). This natural healing power can be observed at work whenever a bruise or a cut heals. Hippocrates taught that a physician's primary task is to remove or reduce the impediments to the proper flow of this healing energy. Let Nature will do the rest.

Hippocrates taught that drugs should be used sparingly and only when absolutely necessary. Of course, in his day, there were only 268 known drugs, all herbal, and treatments were largely preventive medicine, but his first law of healing was — "Above all, don't make things worse." Today, this is known as the Hippocratic Oath.

These days, the Guy in the Woods is usually the last one to be consulted when there's a problem. Most people don't turn to hypnosis first. It's not until they have exhausted conventional options that they even consider hypnosis. By then, the problem has developed deep roots, and surface approaches just won't get the job done.

Surface techniques, like direct suggestion and guided imagery, are suitable for managing symptoms. They're effective at providing comfort or helping a person to cope. For example, a person undergoing medical treatment, receiving chemotherapy, or preparing for the end of life can be helped with surface techniques. But when it comes to emotional issues, a person can't simply imagine themselves into a better belief.

Some hypnotherapists make the mistake of viewing uncomfortable emotions like fear, anger, and sadness as a problem to be gotten rid of. This won't resolve the issue. If anything, it just adds to the internal conflict. Think about it. The Subconscious Mind is the Part of the Mind that holds onto all our memories and emotions.

Emotion is how the Subconscious Mind communicates. If you try to suggest away a feeling, you're going to end up in an argument with the client's Subconscious Mind. That's only going to make things worse.

Why not just let the Subconscious Mind speak?

Surface techniques are effective when applied to surface issues. They also make excellent preliminary techniques to create conditions where healing can happen. For example, to pave the way for the deeper work of regression hypnotherapy by preparing a client to face uncomfortable feelings and memories.

Surface techniques also make effective polishing techniques when you want to enhance or deepen healing. But when a problem is emotional, surface approaches won't get the job done.

You need to find out what the *real* problem is. If you don't, it doesn't matter how many pills you throw at the problem or how many techniques you apply; the client still has the problem. If you fail to resolve the underlying cause of the problem and only treat the symptoms, the problem will persist by expressing through symptoms.

The Symptom Imperative

When surface approaches fail to get rid of the problem, it's because what's visible on the surface isn't really the problem. What the client *thinks* is the problem is just a symptom of the real problem. This is because every symptom serves a subconscious purpose. This Subconscious Mind *requirement* of symptoms is called the Symptom Imperative (SI).

Some believe this purpose is protective by distracting the Conscious Mind from repressed memories and disturbing or overwhelming emotions. But when you're dealing with an emotional issue, protecting the client from their feelings won't get them healed.

Avoiding feelings and memories goes *against* nature. For this reason, Regression to Cause hypnosis works *with* nature by recognizing that human beings are designed to self-heal. But avoidance is always going to be a big part of the problem. After all, those feelings don't feel good! And symptoms are how the Subconscious Mind communicates with the Conscious Mind.

Symptoms make the unconscious conscious. The lump, the bump, the ache, the pain – physical or emotional – is just how the Subconscious Mind makes an important need known to the Conscious Mind. The symptom is a signal. It's coming out of the Subconscious level of Mind and, like a compass, points to the *source* of the problem. And when a person gets triggered, they'll regress.

Regression Happens

Situations in daily life can act as reminders of unresolved experiences from the past. When that happens, the person will get triggered and, either consciously or unconsciously, will relive the original event. We call that a *regression*.

A triggering event causes the Subconscious Mind to return to the unresolved memory in an attempt to *heal* the problem. But the Subconscious Mind doesn't have any more resources to deal with the problem *now* than it did when the problem first arose. That's why it's still a problem. An extreme example of this is a PTSD flashback. This is typically a conscious experience of a disturbing experience from the past being relived.

A nightmare, on the other hand, is an unconscious reliving of an unresolved past experience, often from childhood. A phobia is a partial reliving. Consciously, the person is aware of the fear, but the experience responsible for causing the fear is being relived unconsciously.

While the painful events of youth may be over, the internal conflict continues to rage. When healing doesn't happen naturally, it's because something is preventing it from happening. There's a block. Often this has to do with an unmet need from childhood. The key to healing lies in finding the block, and releasing it, so that Mother Nature can do her thing.

The devil recognizes that the real problem is buried in the client's history. That's where you must go to resolve it. The devil also recognizes that the power isn't in the tool or technique. It's not in the protocol or the Mesmeric power of the practitioner – no matter how persuasive. The *real* power is in the Mind of the client. But to gain access to that power, you need the client's permission to go *there*.

Regression happens. It's natural. But to be successful, you need to make it safe for the client to go where you need them to go and do what you need them to do to find healing.

This is the purpose of the set-up phase. It's to prepare the client by:

1. Satisfying the primary need for safety.
2. Establishing a Contract specifically for regression hypnotherapy.
3. Teaching the client how to be successful in working with you.

This begins with the intake process.

CHAPTER 4:
Conduct the Intake

The devil asked the soldier: "What ails you? You look so unhappy." The soldier answered: "I'm hungry, and I haven't any money."

The intake is where you take a history of the client's presenting issue and is an integral part of preparing the client for the journey you will take together. But if you're like me, you were taught not to waste any time talking with the Conscious Mind. After all, if the Conscious Mind doesn't know how to resolve the problem, why waste any time listening to it?

The advice was to, "Just get them into hypnosis and go to work!" That's fine for surface issues. But when you're dealing with an emotional issue, you need to take the time to listen to what the Conscious Mind has to say. If you don't, you're going to have problems.

The purpose of the intake process isn't merely to establish rapport before diving into the hypnosis. The intake officially marks the beginning of the healing process. Used strategically, it can provide the key information you need to guide the healing process effectively. The intake can support you to:

- Identify how the symptom pattern is expressing.

- Uncover critical issues and concerns that might block the healing process.

- Set the groundwork for the Therapeutic Relationship.

- Enlist the client's cooperation in the healing process.

Taking a history gives the client permission to tell you their Pain Story. This is the Conscious Mind's *tale of woe* about where the client is at *now* – stuck in the Pain of the problem. The Conscious Mind can't fix the problem because it doesn't have the whole Story.

While the Conscious Mind may not have all the information, you still need its cooperation because the Conscious Mind has the power to block you. If you don't give it some time and attention, it will just get in your way because the Conscious Mind needs a sense of control. The reason the client is seeing you is that they don't have control in some area of their life, at least not consciously. Their Subconscious Mind has control. This puts the Conscious and Subconscious Minds at odds with one another. So, there's a conflict.

Your job is to help bring these two parts of the client back into alignment. You can't do that if you dismiss one side in favor of the other. So, work with both. One is not better than the other. Both are integral to the client's well-being. And you must earn the trust of both the Conscious and the Subconscious Minds before proceeding with the healing process.

Regression hypnotherapy requires the cooperation of both the Conscious and Subconscious minds. The client needs to trust you before they will be willing to listen to you or follow your instructions. Allowing the client to tell you their Story about the problem and how it is impacting them in daily life allows the client to feel heard. This builds trust, which lays the foundation for the Therapeutic Relationship.

"People listen better if they feel that you have understood them. They tend to think that those who understand them are intelligent and sympathetic people whose own opinions may be worth listening to. So, if you want the other side to appreciate your interests, begin by demonstrating that you appreciate theirs." – Roger Fisher

Establish the Therapeutic Relationship

Our profession is too quick to toss out the therapeutic value of giving the client permission to speak before diving into the hypnosis. We don't want to be accused of practicing talk therapy. But the Subconscious Mind is the feeling Mind. If you want the Subconscious Mind to trust you, you need to prove that you're someone who will listen to how the client *feels*.

While you're interacting with the Conscious Mind, the Subconscious Mind isn't off somewhere else. It's right there, sitting quietly off to the side, observing you, and deciding whether or *not* you can be trusted. And the Subconscious Mind is duty-bound to protect the client.

Safety is its Prime Directive. It will protect the client from any perceived threat – real or imagined. If you fail to win the trust of the Subconscious Mind, it will protect the client by blocking *you*.

No one cares how much you know, until they know how much you care. - **Don Swartz**

The thing to remember is that the Conscious and Subconscious minds both want the same thing. There is no real separation between these two Parts of the client. It's one Mind. Both serve the same purpose – to be safe. It's just that they have different strategies for fulfilling this important need.

Letting the Conscious Mind tell its tale is a way to prove that you can be trusted. While you're listening, bring attention to how the client feels. Validate those feelings. Show that you won't judge them, that you're not a threat. This speaks directly to the client's Subconscious Mind. That is from where the pain is coming!

Identify the Symptom Pattern

"What ails you?"

The devil's first question is, "What's the problem?" This question speaks to the Conscious Mind of the client. When the soldier answers, "I'm hungry, and I haven't any money," he is not identifying the problem. He is describing how he is experiencing the problem.

This is called the Presenting Issue. *I can't lose the weight . . . I'm worried about money . . . I can't sleep . . . I'm in pain . . . I can't stop . . . I can't start . . . I just got diagnosed . . .* etc. This is how the problem is expressed through symptoms. The question is: What specific patterns are associated with the client's symptoms?

The following questions can help you to identify the symptom pattern:

- What's the problem? Why is it a problem?

- What areas of daily living are impacted by this problem?

- What makes the symptoms worse or better?

- What situations or conditions trigger the symptoms?

- How long has this been a problem?

- When did the problem get started?

- What symptoms were expressing at that time?

- What was happening in the client's life when symptoms first appeared?

Find the Feeling

"Why do you look so unhappy?"

The Presenting Issue identifies what the Conscious Mind *thinks* is the problem. The Symptom Pattern identifies how the real problem is expressing. But it's not the whole problem. It's just the perceived problem. It doesn't matter what the *perceived* problem is, whether it's physical, mental, emotional, or behavioral, the real problem has everything to do with an uncomfortable feeling inside. The devil's next question is, "Why do you look so unhappy?" This speaks directly to the Subconscious Mind. Being *unhappy* is an emotional problem. And the Subconscious Mind is responsible for holding onto all our memories and emotions.

The definition of a symptom is "Something that indicates the existence of something else." Unhappy thoughts and feelings are symptoms of an unresolved, painful life experience. They're meant to be helpful. Every symptom, no matter how painful, is pointing to is a life experience that caused the symptom.

When you're dealing with an emotional issue, encouraging the client to talk about the problem is naturally going to stir up thoughts and feelings that have everything to do with the problem. Important clues as to the underlying cause of the problem can be revealed during the intake – if you care to listen.

The National Guild of Hypnotists states that hypnosis practitioners work with "ordinary, everyday problems." Ordinary everyday people have *emotions*. Emotions drive behavior and find expression through symptoms. So, ordinary, everyday problems are *emotional* problems.

That's the devil's domain.

The devil knows that all things share the same Source. When nourished, each will flourish to reflect that Source. When inhibited or blocked, mutations occur. We call this dis-ease.

Another word for dis-ease is *unhappiness*. A Course in Miracles states, "To heal is to make happy." Healing, then, is about restoring a person to the awareness of their natural state of happiness – physically, mentally, emotionally, and spiritually. It is a return to Love. The underlying problem might have to do with love lost, love denied, or love rejected, but always the root of dis-ease is a lack, an emptiness, an unfulfilled need.

The feeling is never the problem. Feelings and emotions are natural. They're there for a reason. The question is, what's *causing* that specific uncomfortable feeling to express in this way?

"Why do you look so unhappy?"

The devil is all about duality. This is the basis of cause and effect. So, this question has a dual meaning. The problem has to do with how the client is looking at things. It's their lens on life. We call this the Critical Faculty of the Mind (CF).

The Critical Faculty decides what we should pay attention to. It assesses information coming in from our environment through the five senses. It then compares these perceptions with what we already know to be true, based on past experience, so that we'll know how to respond. Good or bad? Comfortable or uncomfortable? Friend or foe? Food or poison?

In brain science, this comparing function of the Critical Faculty is akin to the Reticular Activating System (RAS). The RAS tells us what to pay attention to. For example, when you give a post-hypnotic suggestion to notice the color red-red-red, you are impressing on the RAS the importance of noticing this particular color. As a result of accepting this suggestion, the person will start to see red everywhere.

How we see anything is a function of the Critical Faculty, which acts as a lens through which we see the world of people and things around us. Because its primary function is to keep us consistent with our beliefs, the Critical Faculty ensures that how we see anything is how we see everything.

Experiences shape our beliefs. Our Core Beliefs are formed very early in life and determine how we think, and feel, and respond to the world of people and things around us as adults. So, during the intake, invite your client to talk about childhood. Something must have happened to cause the problem. And everybody has unresolved stuff from childhood.

Every dis-ease is the result of a life experience. – **Dr. Gerd Hamer**

Taking the time to explore the client's formative years can reveal patterns in early life that have everything to do with their presenting issue. Most of the clients I worked with had been dealing with the problem for twenty years or more. Some had been struggling with the issue their whole life. This is pretty typical when it comes to emotional issues.

Emotional problems tend to develop over time. So, unless there's an obvious trauma, the average person won't recognize that there's a problem until they start to see symptoms. Typically, symptoms of an underlying conflict don't appear until mid-life. It just takes that long for the pressure to build up inside. And human beings are hardwired to seek pleasure and avoid pain. The tendency is to ignore the early signs and hope they'll go away.

Unfortunately, this drives the issue deeper underground. So, you need to have realistic expectations about what it's going to take to resolve the client's issue. It's not always going to be a quick fix.

Healing can take time because hypnosis is seldom the first solution most people turn to. By the time they show up on your doorstep, the client has probably been through a gauntlet of outer solutions. By then, they're frustrated or depressed over countless failed attempts to resolve the issue, which just adds to the pain of the problem.

The fact that a problem has been around for a while can actually work in your favor. There's more pressure. More dis-ease can increase the client's motivation to resolve the problem and get some relief. But it also means that the problem has had time to grow and fester, which can add complexity. Complex issues take more time to resolve because there are more moving parts. And to get a lasting result, you need to resolve all the contributing factors.

The process of identifying these factors begins during the intake process. It is a preliminary uncovering procedure that marks the beginning of the healing process. The intake allows you to gather the information you need to guide the healing process effectively. By the end of the intake process, you should have a clear sense of what you're dealing with. From this, you can begin to craft a clearly-defined therapeutic goal for the healing process.

Establish the Therapeutic Goal

The client's therapeutic goal acts as a compass. It keeps you on track by pointing you in the direction you need to go. Everything points to this one thing. And yet, too many hypnotherapists fail to give this the attention that it warrants. You need a clearly-defined therapeutic goal to guide the healing process effectively.

Clients will come to you with a long list of problems. To be successful, you need to focus attention on one specific issue. Before you proceed any further, make sure that you elicit a clear statement of what the client's specific desired outcome is. What problem are you trying to resolve? Pick one and focus on that. This becomes your north star.

- What result does the client hope to achieve?

- How will they know when they get there?

- What does *free of the problem look like?*

If the client has multiple issues, make a list. Look for the Symptom Pattern. How did the problem develop? What symptom came on first?

Many of the client's symptoms will be connected. This means that resolving the first symptom can remove other issues, as if by magic! Which problem has the most significant emotional charge to it? That's the problem generating the most internal pressure. Resolving this problem will get your client the most bang for their therapeutic buck.

The best place to begin the healing process will flow naturally out of the intake process. As the client talks about their history with the problem, you'll start to identify certain patterns that will point to the best place to proceed. This is something of an intuitive process, but there really is no right or wrong way to go about it. Sometimes, it's just a matter of asking the client, "Which issue would you like to work on first?"

Identify the Conditions for Change

The client's Therapeutic Goal gives you a destination. How you get there will depend on what specific conditions are contributing to the client's issue. If the client's issue involves unwanted behaviors or people, you need to identify what or who they might be. Make a list. What needs to change for the client to be happy? For example, if you are working on a behavioral issue like weight loss, the client already knows what they should be doing. They just haven't been able to do it. That's why they need your help.

The purpose of defining the Conditions for Change is to make the client responsible for the results. While the goal of therapeutic hypnosis is effortless change, the client still needs to be willing to participate. You can make it easier for them to take action. But you can't do it for them. So, ask them to give you a list of specific actions or behaviors that they believe will contribute to their success.

Not every issue requires behavioral changes. But the Conditions for Change list can give you a way to test the client's expectations. Ask what would need to happen for their goal statement to come true? Are they expecting you to wave your magic wand and make them change?

If so, you need to address that. Hypnosis isn't magic. The Conditions for Change need to be realistic. This means that if the client says that what needs to happen is for them to be able to eat two large pizzas and a gallon of ice-cream at every meal, there's a problem. You can't override the laws of Nature.

Creating a list of Conditions for Change allows you to identify specific problem areas, test your results, and formulate suggestions you can use to wrap up your sessions. What or who needs to change for the client to achieve their goal? Where are the stumbling blocks?

Identify the Benefits of Change

The intake process is not merely about the problem. It's also about the rewards of having done the work necessary to create lasting change. So, what are the rewards the client hopes to enjoy for having made this change? What is his vision for the future? How does it feel to be moving in this direction?

The therapeutic goal tells you what the client wants as a result of doing this work with you. Their Conditions for Change tell you what needs to happen so that they can have it. The benefits list tells you the motivating factor. So, how is their life going to improve as a result of achieving this goal?

How will they know that they've arrived at their destination? How when they feel when they look in the mirror and realize they have made this change? What will other people think? How will they respond differently to certain situations in life?

Getting rid of the pain of the problem just isn't sufficiently motivating for most people. The rewards need to spark passion and enthusiasm. That's what will keep the client committed long enough to achieve their goal.

What does a brighter day look like for the future? What does "happy" look like for the client? How will he know when he has "arrived" at his desired destination? What is waiting there for him, now? That's where the juice is at! Make a list because you can use them to formulate targeted suggestions at the end of each session.

Summary

The Intake Process marks the beginning of the healing process. It is a preliminary uncovering process that allows you to establish the Therapeutic Relationship and identify the key information you need to guide the healing process.

Symptom Resolution Keys

1. How is the problem expressing as a Symptom Pattern?
2. What emotions are connected to the problem?
3. What is the client's Therapeutic Goal?
4. What specific conditions will support the client in achieving this goal?
5. What are the desired rewards for making these changes?

The Intake Process also allows you to uncover the specific information you'll need to educate the client about the process in a way that is relevant to his specific problem, concerns, and desired results.

Learn more in the Strategic Intake Process Course here: www.tribeofhealers.com/ready-for-regression-first-session-system-course

A Miracle is a correction in how we perceive and how we think. The effect of a miracle is healing. – **The 50 Principles of A Course in Miracles**

CHAPTER 5:
Educate the Client

The Devil said: "If you'll hire yourself out to me and be my serving man, you shall have enough to last you the rest of your life. But there are some conditions. You'll have to serve me for seven years, and after that you'll be free.

Your educational pre-talk is an integral part of the overall healing process. It is laying the foundation for you and the client to work together successfully by setting the tone for a deeper level of intimacy. It needs to be personalized for each client.

The purpose of your educational pre-talk is to establish a Therapeutic Contract for the work you will do together. It needs to speak directly to the client's Therapeutic Goal and what will be required of the client to achieve that goal.

The devil always requires a contract. For the Contract to be binding requires *informed* consent from the client. This is why the Intake Process comes first. The intake gives you the information that you need to customize your educational pre-talk specifically for the client.

Some hypnosis practitioners send their clients a pre-recorded pre-talk prior to the first session. While this can save time in the first session, it's too generic to be of any value in a therapeutic setting. Everything you deliver in your educational pre-talk should be about the client. It should speak directly to the client's specific issue and concerns. Make it an interactive process, and you'll make the client a partner in their own healing!

Educational Pre-Talk

The following three core concepts can help you to prepare your clients specifically for the transformational healing work of regression to cause hypnotherapy.

#1. How the Mind Works

Educating the client begins with teaching them how the Mind works. This helps to remove some of the unknowns that can generate fear and apprehension about the hypnosis. But you can also use your Mind Model to get rid of resistance to "going there" by showing the client where you will be guiding them.

No one really knows how the Mind works (or even if such a thing exists!), but there are many useful models that can help you to better understand the territory in which you will lead your clients.

Freud's Iceberg Model

The Mind Model that seems to work best for most clients is also the simplest. This is Freud's Iceberg Mind Model, which divides the Mind into two distinct levels. The visible part of the iceberg represents the *Conscious* or Thinking level of the Mind. Below the surface is the vastly larger *Subconscious Mind* or Feeling level of the Mind which holds onto our history in the form of memories and emotions, both good and bad.

The Subconscious Mind is the level of Mind that is not fully accessible to the Conscious Mind because the Conscious Mind resides on the surface of awareness. It interfaces with our external world and is concerned primarily with meeting important needs by seeking, analyzing, and evaluating objects, people, and situations. It then decides on the best course of action to satisfy those needs.

Our most basic needs are physiological. Air, water, food, shelter, sex, warmth, rest, etc. are essential to survival. Hunger is a need for physical nourishment. But we can also have psychological hunger. We can yearn for social connection, emotional fulfillment, creative self-expression.

When physiological needs are adequately met, we begin striving to satisfy psychological needs such as safety and security; belonging, love and intimacy, esteem, respect, and prestige.

When psychological needs are adequately met, we begin seeking to self-actualize through personal growth, peak experiences, self-fulfillment, and creative self-expression.

Omni-Hypnosis Model

The Omni-Hypnosis Mind Model, developed by Gerald Kein, divides the Mind into three concentric circles:

1. Unconscious Mind (UCM)
2. Subconscious Mind (SCM)
3. Conscious Mind (CM)

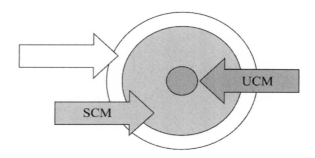

The Conscious Mind

The *Conscious Mind* is the relatively narrow, outermost band of the circle. This contains the analytical, rational functions of Mind. This Part of the Mind is concerned with outer things. Its job is to make sense of what's going on in our environment so we can respond appropriately. To do this, the Conscious Mind uses thinking and reasoning and analysis to come up with solutions to problems.

The ability to use thinking and reasoning is very useful when it comes to making out a grocery list, balancing the checkbook, or figuring out an eating plan. But when it comes to dealing with feelings, the Conscious Mind is at a disadvantage. This is because the Conscious Mind doesn't do feelings. It just *thinks*. Feeling is the territory of the Subconscious Mind.

The Subconscious Mind

Behind the Conscious Mind is a much larger circle. This Part of the Mind is the repository of our life history. The *Subconscious Mind* holds onto all our memories and how they made us feel. These learning experiences shape our beliefs, habits, and protective programming.

These Subconscious programs are meant to empower us by helping us to take care of our own needs. Unfortunately, stuff can happen early in life to cause a person to lose touch with themselves. As a result, we can forget who we really are and how to feel good about ourselves. This happens to everyone to varying degrees. For some, it can make the Mind a living hell.

The Subconscious is not only a place of bad memories and fear-based emotions. It's also a place of love and healing. Through the healing process of regression hypnotherapy, it is possible to recover powerful sources of fulfillment and empowerment such as:

- Unrealized gifts

- Unique talents

- Life purpose

- Calling in life

The Unconscious Mind

At the *deepest* level, there's a Part of us that never changes. Sometimes called the *Unconscious Mind*, the innermost circle is not always accessible to conscious awareness. This Part of the Mind is responsible for the autonomic functions of the body, the immune function, and memories of past lives. It's also the Part of the Mind that contains our source code for happiness and happiness and well-being.

It's basic human nature to seek to be happy, whole, and complete. It's in our design. The blueprint is right there at the center, where we remain exactly as we were designed by Source. Our capacity to feel good and happy and loving towards ourselves and others never changes.

This is the well-spring through which core states can be accessed. Core states such as beingness, freedom, love, peace, and oneness are intrinsic to our nature. They exist and can be experienced independently of external conditions. This is the source of healing.

The Critical Faculty

Between the Conscious Mind and the Subconscious Mind lies a semipermeable barrier called the *Critical Faculty* of the Mind. This Part of the Mind acts as a gatekeeper to the Subconscious Mind, filtering out information that does not match our already-established beliefs.

The Critical Faculty is concerned primarily with survival. It's there to protect us by keeping us congruent with our already-accepted beliefs. It's also what gives us our unique lens on life. The Critical determines our personal point of view, and it's all based on what we learned from our experiences growing up.

The Critical Faculty is not fully formed until around age five. Before that, there really isn't any separation between the Conscious and Subconscious Minds. During these developmental years, the Child is literally downloading information from the environment. This makes the Mind of the Childlike a super-learning computer.

While the Mind of a child is wide open to learning, the younger the child is, the less information available with which to interpret what's happening. The interpretations of a Child are often inaccurate because the child lacks experience. There is insufficient data with which to compare new experiences. As a result, ideas can be accepted uncritically.

As children, we received a lot of messages from our environment. The things that were said or done to us, what was modeled by those around us – parents, siblings, teachers, those in authority – and how those things made us feel, made impressions. Based on these impressions, we made decisions. These decisions formed the basis of our beliefs.

Our earliest experiences formed our Core Beliefs, which have to do with identity and what to expect in life. They tell us how we must be or not be in order to get our needs met and survive. This gives us a sense of normalcy and security. It tells us how to respond to situations in life, giving us a sense of control.

The Critical Faculty is our Belief System. Unfortunately, not everything we believe is necessarily true. Many of our beliefs are outdated because they were established to meet our needs at a much younger age. They're based on the decisions of a child.

It's been said that more learning occurs in the first two years of life than will happen over the rest of a person's life. This is because unconscious learning doesn't involve thinking or analysis. Being able to input data very quickly gives us an evolutionary advantage in terms of survival, but it can block us from getting what we want later in life. This is because many of the beliefs that formed early in life are simply not true. And our beliefs decide what we're going to get in life.

#2. How Hypnosis Works

Hypnosis is *not* what most people think. Most people don't know anything about hypnosis. Even when they think they know what hypnosis is, they're usually carrying around some myths and misconceptions. So, once you have shown the client how their Mind works, educate them about how hypnosis works. If you leave it up to the client, they'll just assume. Make sure they know what to expect.

There are lots of definitions of hypnosis, but even hypnosis professionals can't agree on what, exactly, hypnosis is. For the purposes of educating the client, it's best to just keep things simple.

Technically, hypnosis has to do with bypassing the Critical Faculty of the Mind. But that's too fancy-pants for most clients. All the client really needs to know is that hypnosis is a state of *focused attention* where thinking and analyzing are set aside. This tells the client what to do.

When the Thinking Part of the Mind agrees to take a back seat, the Feeling Part of Mind can step forward, allowing you to interact with it. The client needs to know this. They also need to know when the hypnosis is happening. If you don't tell them what to expect when they're hypnotized, they'll be pre-occupied with thinking, *Am I hypnotized? Or Is it happening?* That just gets in the way.

You need the client to set aside thinking and analyzing. If they're trying to figure out whether or not the hypnosis is happening, that will *prevent* the hypnosis from happening. That won't help you to get the results you want. So, you need to tell them what to expect.

#3. How You Will Work Together

Teaching the client how you will work together is setting up for the regression work. To be successful, you need the client's full cooperation. You need a conscious agreement from them to set aside the need to control. Without it, the Conscious Mind will just get in your way. So, remind the client that healing happens – when we *let* it.

The way out of the problem is to gain access the Part of the Mind that knows how the problem got started and has the power to heal. That's the Subconscious Mind. The Subconscious Mind is the Feeling Mind. And to gain access to the underlying cause of the problem, we need that mental activity to be set aside - at least to begin with.

The client must be willing to set aside thinking, and reasoning, and logic and pay attention to the feelings instead. Get the client's agreement to let the Thinking Part of them sit off on the sidelines and take on the role of Observer.

Let the client know that it's okay to suspend judgment temporarily. They can think about it later if they want to. But for now, that Thinking Part of them needs to be willing to stand aside and just be curious about what they might learn through the process.

The Adult, Thinking Part of the client is an important component of the healing process, too. It's just taking a back seat for the time being. When the time comes, you will call upon this Part of the client to assist in the process. But until then, you need it to take a back seat.

Instruct the client to:

1.   Follow instructions.

2.   Respond quickly.

3.   Go with his first impression. That's the feeling.

You need their attention to be on the inside, on feelings and sensations in the body. That's how the Subconscious Mind communicates. Remind the client that we're dealing with the irrational Part of the Mind. It doesn't have to make sense; later, it will all make sense. Just keep the focus on the feeling. Make it clear. "When I ask you a question, I don't want you to *think* the answer. I want you to feel the answer." That's where the healing lies.

Establish "The Contract"

The devil's Contract is comprised of the following four basic elements:

1.   The offer

2.   The consideration

3.   The terms and conditions

4.   Acceptance of the offer

The Offer

The offer is the promise one party makes to pay the other for their services.

"Enough to last you the rest of your life."

The devil's offer is not to manage the symptoms. That's like using Stop Leak when what the client really needs is a new radiator. The goal of regression hypnotherapy is not a temporary improvement; it's a complete resolution of the problem.

The Consideration

Consideration is what is given in exchange for the agreed-upon outcome.

"If you'll hire yourself out to me and be my serving man . . ."

The Contract for regression hypnotherapy has two parts.

1. Hypnosis
2. Regression to Cause

The devil is saying, "If you want to work with me (hire yourself out to me), you'll have to follow my instructions and do things my way (be my serving-man)." The Contract for hypnosis requires the client's permission to allow you to guide them into hypnosis by following your instructions. But hypnosis only gives you access to the Subconscious level of Mind. To achieve a lasting result, the client must be willing to do the work necessary.

Regression hypnotherapy is not a passive process. It requires the client's participation. And you need the client's permission to revisit painful memories and emotions. Without it, you're going to have problems. To be successful, the client must be willing to go where you need them to go and do what you need them to do when you tell them.

You can't just do it for the client.

It takes consciousness to heal consciousness. You can't just suggest away an emotion. And avoiding uncomfortable memories from the past just keeps them trapped inside. That's what's generating the symptoms. The client must be willing to allow uncomfortable feelings to be a part of the process. They must be prepared to face uncomfortable memories and emotions and to disclose painful or shameful truths that may be revealed through the process. That's ground zero.

The Terms & Conditions

The term refers to the period of time during which The Contract is in effect. The Conditions define the rights and responsibilities of both parties.

"But one thing I must tell you, and that is, during those seven years you must not wash, or comb, or cut your hair, or trim your beard, or pare your nails, or wipe the water from your eyes."

The goal of educating the client is to establish Positive Mental Expectancy (PME) regarding the healing process. But PME doesn't happen during the pre-talk. It happens during the client's first hypnosis session. You're just setting up for it to happen by telling the client what to expect.

The biggest mistake that too many hypnosis practitioners make is making what we do mysterious. You need to be upfront about what's going to happen before you begin the induction. Cloak and dagger tactics are outdated. They are definitely NOT client-centered. And in a therapeutic setting, they are largely unethical. Be transparent about what's going to happen.

Gerry Kein's advice was, "Tell 'em, tell 'em, tell 'em." Tell the client what's going to happen. Tell them why it's going to happen. Tell them how allowing these things to happen will benefit them. Make what you're asking the client to do safe and reasonable, and you'll make the client a willing partner in their own healing.

Seven Years

A term of seven years is not a randomly chosen time period. The devil is requiring a commitment to the healing process. To achieve a complete and lasting resolution of the problem can take time. This is a contract for real and lasting change. And regression hypnotherapy is not a quick fix technique. It's a process through which real and lasting change can be achieved.

In order to come to completion and restore wholeness can take time because many of the issues we deal with have roots in experiences in childhood, particularly prior to age seven. In the growth and development of a child, the first seven years involve significant physical, cognitive, emotional, and social development.

For example, by age seven, most children have a sense of time. They become more aware of and sensitive to the feelings of others, a trait called empathy. And while the child has overcome many of the fears they had when they were younger, they worry about others' opinions and can still fear the unknown. As a result, going to a new school can generate significant stress for a seven-year-old.

Certain numbers recur in sacred literature because they are associated with specific ideas. The number seven was considered sacred to many cultures, including the Persians, who viewed the devil as God's twin brother. To the Hebrews, seven represents the union between the Divine (3) and Man (4), between Spirit and Matter.

Seven is a number of completion or wholeness. There are seven days in Creation, which are reflected in the seven days of the week. Seven represents a full cycle.

Interestingly, the number seven is associated with the letter G (zayin), which is an arrow. The original meaning is a weapon signifying both a *distance to be traveled* and war. War means the rejection of identity, an internal conflict.

To "do seven times" signifies an oath bearing the seal of sanctity. That's a Contract! The Devil's Therapy involves a seven-phase protocol. In some cases, all seven phases can be completed in a single session. More often, the client will require multiple sessions to get a complete resolution of the problem. This is because there can be multiple aspects, multiple events, and multiple causes generating the symptoms.

Don't Wash

One of the key conditions of the Therapeutic Contract is allowing uncomfortable feelings and emotions to come to conscious awareness. The devil isn't telling the client to forgo personal grooming. He's saying, *"Don't cut off your feelings!"*

To get the healing, the client must be willing to let their feelings come up and come out and be expressed fully. The devil doesn't hide the fact that it's going to get uncomfortable. He's disclosing that working with him, you must be prepared to get honest and allow yourself to feel your feelings.

As children, we were taught to avoid our *bad* feelings. We learned to suck in our gut, acquire the proper attitude, and march in step to an internal voice that commands, *Don't think, don't speak, don't feel.* But being a tough little soldier is a big part of the problem.

Feelings and emotions are natural. It's the resistance to feeling the feeling that causes the discomfort. The devil teaches the client to pay attention to what's happening in their body and to allow uncomfortable feelings and emotions to express.

To resist is to not let in. The opposite of resistance is love. -
Thorwald Dethlefsen

Basically, we only have two feelings. One feels good. The other doesn't feel so good. That's it. We're either in a state of contraction or expansion. In an expanded state, we feel good. The body feels relaxed, warm, and open. We feel safe, contented, happy, peaceful, loving, free, and alive. Contraction is felt as physical tension, tightness, and pain.

Emotions are how the Subconscious Mind communicates through the body. Emotions like fear, anxiety, anger, resentment, sadness, loneliness, and guilt can be found and felt in the body – usually in the gut, chest, or throat, but they can also be felt in the neck, shoulders, legs – anywhere in the body, really.

The Devil's Therapy is not just another masking and avoiding technology. This is different. The client is going to have to be willing to roll up his shirt sleeves and get dirty. That means letting those uncomfortable feelings come to the surface of awareness where they can be acknowledged, accepted, and released. Once an uncomfortable feeling has been brought to awareness, it can be released. Embracing the feeling, fully releases the feeling, restoring the client's ability to feel good again.

Don't Cut Your Hair or Beard

Remember the story of Samson and Delilah? Samson is a big, strong, hairy guy who falls in love with the harlot, Delilah. Delilah, whose name means "one who weakened or uprooted or impoverished," seduces Samson. Samson, who has long, beautiful hair, falls asleep after his tryst with Delilah and, while he sleeps, Delilah cuts off his hair.

Remember the seven years? An oath bearing the seal of sanctity is to do seven times. Samson has taken an ascetic vow, which includes refraining from cutting his hair or beard. When Delilah cuts off all seven locks of Samson's hair, she robs him of his spiritual strength.

Like Samson, we've been seduced by the world at the cost of our authentic self. Repression disconnects us from our core integrity. In cutting ourselves off from our feelings, we have lost touch with our inner *strength*, the power which is the source of our health, happiness, and well-being.

Letting your hair down means to relax, let go, be natural, uninhibited, authentic. The requirement to not cut the hair is to set aside thinking, analyzing, judging, and trying to figure things out, and give your Authentic Self permission to express.

The beard, when permitted to grow, is a symbol of maturity, signifying knowledge, and wisdom. The highest human goal – whether we call it wisdom or enlightenment – is to accept everything. It's the realization that everything is perfectly fine, just as they are. This is what is meant by true self-knowledge. It's realizing you're okay, just as you are.

What other people think of you is none of your business. As long as there is anything that still disturbs you or that you feel needs changing, you have not yet attained self-knowledge. The Truth is there's nothing wrong with you. You were designed, by Nature, to express health and happiness. You were designed to self-heal. So, if there's a problem, it's because something happened to interrupt your natural, internal programming for health and happiness. The devil knows this. He also knows that whatever happened, God meant it for good. Every cloud has a silver lining. With every curse comes a blessing. And behind every symptom is hidden a positive purpose. The challenge in looking into the past is to find the gifts in the emotional garbage.

Don't Pare Your Nails

Cutting your fingernails is a way of giving attention to personal appearances. Healing requires turning away from externals and the appearance of things to look deeply inward. When nails are allowed to grow, they become claws, a sign of aggression. Children are taught to suppress their aggressive feelings and *be nice*. This social conditioning plays a big part in the development of dis-ease. Whatever has been stuffed down, rejected, avoided, abandoned must be allowed to come out and be given permission to express.

Don't Wipe Your Eyes

Emotional release work is an important part of the healing process of regression hypnotherapy. It's what allows the client to come to clarity and make newer, healthier choices. Eyes symbolize consciousness. It's been said that the eyes are mirrors of the soul. A variant of this proverb is the *eyes are the window of the soul.*

Eyes both perceive what's happening and communicate emotions. So, what we see and how we feel are intimately connected. Our conscious awareness of our environment is based on our five sensory perceptions – seeing, hearing, smelling, tasting, touching, and feeling. How we perceive anything determines how we feel. A positive perception will generate feelings of comfort and well-being. A negative perception will generate feelings of discomfort and emotions like fear, sadness, and anger. The Subconscious Mind is the emotional Mind, so we want the client to pay attention to feelings and emotions.

Most of us were conditioned to dismiss or ignore uncomfortable feelings and emotions. We learned to use thinking to override the truth of how we feel. While this allowed us to soldier on as children, habitually ignoring our biological feedback system eventually takes a toll. In time, those unresolved emotions will find expression through physical, mental, and emotional dis-ease.

Word-famous leprosy surgeon Dr. Paul Brand discovered that people with leprosy do not have rotten flesh. They have an inability to feel their feelings physically. The disease causes the blood flow to get cut off from key parts of the body resulting in the death of nerve endings. As the nerve endings die, the person loses the ability to feel pain.

Not being able to feel pain can lead to serious complications. For example, lepers tend to go blind because they cannot feel the uncomfortable sensations that cause us to blink. When a person puts a lid on their emotions, the feelings get trapped inside. This can lead to symptoms such as:

- Depression
- Grief
- Anxiety
- Difficulty feeling emotions

- Eating disorders

- Addiction to food, alcohol, drugs, gambling, pornography, etc.

- Procrastination

- People-pleasing

- Trust issues

- Relationship problems

- Controlling behavior

- Avoidance behavior

- Blaming

- Self-criticism

- Abuse

- Self-sabotage

- Money issues

- Obsessive thoughts

The client must be willing to allow feelings and emotions to be a part of the process. "Don't try to wipe away the truth of how you feel. Don't deny your deepest feelings." Tears – whether of sadness, anger, grief, or joy – must be brought to conscious awareness and allowed to express.

The Acceptance

"The soldier replied, 'If it can't be helped, I may as well get started.'

Acceptance is when the other party agrees to perform the task for the compensation specified in The Contract.

The devil lays it out right from the start. There's no sales pitch, no deception. He's not allowed to work that way, contrary to popular belief. The devil must follow nature. So, he tells the soldier, *If you want to get better, you're going to have to do the work. The question is, are you willing to let yourself feel your truest feelings? Are you ready to give yourself permission to release those uncomfortable feelings so you can feel better?*

And what does the soldier reply? *If it can't be helped, I may as well get started.* Not much of a hurrah! is it? The client's acceptance of the agreement is more an act of resignation than an act of will. That's a problem. Desiring to heal is not the same as being willing to do what's necessary to allow healing. Some people just want a pill. They're not really willing to make the life changes required to achieve the lasting results they want.

This is why The Contract is so important to your success. The goal of *lasting* change is accomplished through a process of restoring internal balance and harmony. Nature will do the rest. It takes as long as it takes *to get the healing.* That's the Contract. You're not just guiding the client into hypnosis and delivering a few suggestions. Regression hypnotherapy requires more of the client. So, your educational pre-talk needs to be more comprehensive than your basic hypnosis pre-talk.

Regression hypnotherapy is a journey of self-discovery that will take the client into uncharted territory. The client must be prepared to allow uncomfortable thoughts, and feelings, and memories to come to awareness. And many of the issues you'll work with will be rooted in unresolved, traumatic experiences from the past. Understandably, most people do not want to go there. But research shows that the only effective way to resolve a traumatic memory for good is to face the feelings trapped inside the memory. This is the work of the devil.

Healing is accomplished the instant the sufferer no longer sees any value in pain. – **A Course in Miracles**

Hans's seeming lack of enthusiasm does not mean he is being difficult. It's just that he has been conditioned to view reality mechanistically. So, when faced with chronic physical or emotional problems, his tendency is to look for a *mechanic* who will administer the necessary treatment while he lies back passively. He just wants the symptoms to go away.

The problem with this attitude is that healing is an *inside* job. You can't fix the Mind from the outside. And the one place our soldier hasn't looked is within. What's inside are feelings and memories he hasn't been willing to look at. No wonder he's reluctant to go there! He doesn't want to *have* to feel, to know, to be. It's just that he's already exhausted all other avenues. What other option is there? So, if there's no other way, if it can't be helped, he reasons, might as well get started . . . even if that means facing the dragon.

You can work with that. It's here that any devil worth his salt would seal the deal by affirming how *awful* it has been having to go through life feeling so BAD, so out of control, powerless, hopeless, scared, and alone – *over and over and over again*. The devil would then remind the client that there's a good reason for him feeling that way. He would remind the client that, regardless of changes in circumstance and the passage of time, decades sometimes, the feeling is still there.

That feeling is what's calling for resolution. And it is connected to every time the client ever felt that way. That feeling goes all the way back to the very *first time*, the client felt that feeling. That's where we must go to find the healing. That's the Contract you're after. *We go where we need to go to get the healing.*

Never proceed with hypnosis until you have a binding Contract. If the client says or implies, "Yes, I guess if I have to," isn't sufficient motivation to proceed. Believe me, it will just come back to bite you in the butt later. You need to identify, acknowledge, and resolve any client reluctance before you proceed with the healing process.

What you're after is a 100% *Yes! I want to be free of this!* So, if the client is holding out hope for some external solution such as medication or surgery and is merely willing to try hypnosis, they're simply not ready to proceed. They're not sufficiently invested in the results to be successful.

They don't have to be enthralled about allowing uncomfortable memories and emotions to come to awareness. Nobody is. But they do need to be committed to achieving complete healing. To accomplish this, you need a contract for both the hypnosis and the therapeutic process of regression to cause.

Resistance

The client's acceptance of the Contract must allow both the hypnosis and the regression therapy. Without it, you're going to have to deal with resistance.

In sessions, resistance can show up as:

- resistance to being hypnotized

- resistance to experiencing uncomfortable feelings

- resistance to reviewing painful past events

- resistance to admitting shameful truths

- resistance to feeling uncomfortable feelings

Resistance does not mean that the client is being difficult. It's simply evidence that you don't yet have a Contract that allows *that* (whatever you're bumping into) to be a part of the process. You need both Conscious and Subconscious permission to guide the process.

The Conscious Mind can throw up resistance because you're asking the client to consciously face something he's been trying to avoid. The Conscious Mind needs to have a good reason to hand over control and allow you to guide the healing process.

The Subconscious can generate resistance because it is duty-bound to protect the client from any threat, real or imagined. The Subconscious Mind needs to feel safe in cooperating and revealing sensitive information which, in the past, was frightening or overwhelming for the client. You can do away with a lot of unnecessary resistance simply by using your educational pre-talk to satisfy these important needs.

Secondary Gain

Resistance does not mean that the client is holding onto the problem because it somehow benefits them. Blaming the client won't get them healed. So, really hear this: resistance is fear. Human beings naturally fear the unknown. And secondary gain is always second to the primary gain.

If you focus on resolving the *primary* gain, most of the time, the secondary gain will either fall away or be a fairly easy fix. The primary gain is almost always one of safety. That's the Subconscious Mind's Prime Directive – to protect. When you bump into resistance, find the feeling and focus on *that fear*. That becomes the next step.

This is the work of regression hypnotherapy! Resistance is a block. It's there for a reason, but it's preventing the client from healing. So, make the client responsible for the results. Remind them, "I can't do this for you!" Make sure that you have a Contract that allows the next step, and the next step will happen easily.

Summary

The purpose of the educational pre-talk is to establish a binding contract that allows you to guide the healing process. Because regression hypnotherapy requires more of the client, your educational pre-talk needs to be more comprehensive than what's needed for the standard Hypnosis Contract.

The Hypnosis Contract merely requires an agreement from the client to allow hypnosis to happen by setting aside thinking and following instructions. The Contract for Regression Hypnotherapy, on the other hand, requires the client to be an active participant in the process of creating change from the inside out. To achieve a lasting result, the client must be willing to:

1. Allow you to guide the process by following instructions.
2. Commit to a process of facilitated self-healing.

3. Allow uncomfortable memories and feelings to come to awareness.

4. Keep the focus on feelings.

Learn more in the Educational Pre-Talk Course here: www.tribeofhealers.com/ready-for-regression-first-session-system-course

Working with me, hypnosis is simply the shift from thinking to feeling.
— **Randy Shaw, Advanced Hypnotherapy of Utah**

CHAPTER 6:
Test & Prepare for Regression

S
o, off he went with the little man, who led him straight to hell. There, the devil told him what to do - tend the fires under the caldrons where the damned souls are cooking; clean the house; carry the sweepings behind the back door, and, in general, keep order.

To the ancients, hell was a dark, mysterious, and awesome place. It wasn't a place of fire and brimstone or the punishment for sins. In Egypt, the underworld was a place of judgment and rebirth. Egyptian pictures of the wicked being destroyed in the fire pits of the underworld represented the enemies of the sun god (light). These spirits of darkness, being burned by the fiery light of sunrise and sunset, were interpreted by early Christians as the torments of damned souls.

Psychologically, hell is the Shadow Realm. This is the territory of the Subconscious Mind where everything we have denied and judged against has been banished from conscious awareness. This makes the Mind a living hell.

What's cooking in hell is every unacceptable impulse; everything we have refused to accept, including our unrealized potential, lies within us –buried alive. That which we condemn – in ourselves or others – may be out of sight, but it's never out of mind. And the more we repress and try to avoid, the more havoc these things will wreak in our lives.

The Subconscious level of Mind is where all the trouble is brewing. That's where we must go to resolve the problem. But before you start regressing the client into painful past events, you need to prepare the client for the work you will do together. You can't just do it for them.

The devil makes the client responsible for the results. Make sure your client is ready, willing, and able to do the work required to be successful by teaching them what to do. As hypnosis is the optimum state for learning, begin by guiding the client into hypnosis.

The Hypnosis

There are many ways to induce hypnosis, but the objective is to set aside the critical thinking part of the Mind in order to gain access to the irrational, feeling part of the Mind. The late Dave Elman defined hypnosis as "The bypass of the critical function of the Conscious Mind followed by selective acceptable suggestion."

The Subconscious Mind is the emotional Mind, so the quickest way to induce hypnosis is to provoke an uncomfortable feeling. But in the first session, it's best not to dump the client into their stuff. Before you start regressing a client into painful events from the past, make sure that the client is willing to:

1. Follow your instructions.

2. Allow uncomfortable emotions to come to consciousness.

That's The Contract.

In a therapeutic setting, hypnosis is really the least important part of the session. People don't pay for hypnosis. They pay for results. You don't want to waste a lot of your session time on the induction. You want to get the client into hypnosis and then get to work on the problem. Before you can do this, you need a client who is convinced that the hypnosis happened and who can enter into a state of somnambulism very quickly.

Real regression requires somnambulism. Somnambulism allows revivification of past events, not merely recall. You need to test for depth. You also need to provide proof that the client is hypnotized because that's what they *think* they're paying for. Remember, the client is invested in hypnosis being the solution. Their belief that the desired change is going to happen depends on their conviction that the hypnosis happened.

If the client opens their eyes at the end of the session and says, "I don't think I was hypnotized," you won't get the results you were after. So, don't skip these two important steps. Test for state and provide a Convincer.

I use the Elman Induction in the first session because it can be adapted for any client. It converts easily into a relaxation induction or a rapid induction and has a built-in test for the threshold of somnambulism, which is amnesia through suggestion. Another test for the threshold of somnambulism is glove anesthesia. This test can double as a Convincer to prove to the client that they are really and truly hypnotized.

You don't need relaxation for hypnosis, but most people don't have any resistance to relaxing. For the first session, I like to use a relaxation induction. Guiding a client to relax into hypnosis gives you more time to observe responses, allowing you to adapt to the needs of the client. The feelings and sensations of increasing relaxation offer proof that hypnosis is safe while ensuring that the client's first session with you is enjoyable. You can then use these experiences to establish positive expectations toward future sessions.

Once the client is in somnambulism, I use the state to condition the client for a rapid induction. I then teach the client how to perform the following four tasks, which are a part of the healing process of regression hypnotherapy.

The Tasks

The tasks in hell are four universal healing steps. These are used by healers throughout the world and apply to any healing intervention, whether it's energy-based, emotion-based, or good old-fashioned physical healing.

I was first introduced to these steps back in the early nineties when I took basic training in Pranic Healing. Pranic Healing is an energy-based modality that encourages healing by removing toxic or blocked energy from the mind-body system and replacing it with life-force energy or *prana*. The four-step Pranic Healing protocol is:

1. Sense
2. Cleanse
3. Energize
4. Seal

First, you **sense** the area of the wound. E.g., physical or emotional pain, tension, tightness, inflammation, infection.

Next, you **cleanse** the wound to remove toxic debris, which might prevent healing from happening. E.g., dirt, sliver, pus, toxic thought, and emotional energies.

You would then **energize** the area just cleansed by filling the void with positive energy. E.g., antiseptic, Pranic energy, statements of validation, positive imagery. This helps to encourage the natural healing process.

The final step is to **seal** the area just cleansed and energized. This puts a layer of protection over the freshly treated wound site to prevent reinfection while nature does her thing. E.g., apply a bandage, fill with blue light, guided imagery, and positive suggestions for change.

These four steps correspond with the devil's instructions to tend the fire, clean house, carry the sweepings, and keep order.

#1. Tend the Fire

To tend means to "pay attention to." What's bubbling and boiling in the pot is a feeling inside that the client just doesn't like. What's keeping the Pain Story alive is the fire burning beneath the cauldron. That's the Symptom Imperative.

Often, by the time a client comes to you, they're in real pain, physically or emotionally. Pain plays an important role in alerting us to a problem. That's its purpose. So, the first step is to pay attention to the uncomfortable feeling by focusing on the body. That's where we feel our feelings.

Symptoms are uncomfortable. It might be a lump, a bump, an ache, or a pain, but the symptom is an insistent signal coming out of an event that caused it. *That feeling* has everything to do with the problem. Focusing on the feeling is like putting more wood on the fire. It amplifies the feeling, making it stronger. Amplifying a feeling brings more of it to conscious awareness. This is setting up to ensure you get a strong bridge to the event that caused the problem. Tend the fire means to focus on the feeling.

#2. Clean House

When we've come to the end of our tether, true freedom calls for a clean sweep. To clean house means to get rid of everything you don't want. A house is where you love. The place we live in is in our Mind. This means releasing all the thoughts and feelings that are contributing to the problem. This isn't about trying to get rid of the feeling. It's about honoring the feeling and giving it permission to express.

The only place a feeling can hurt us is trapped inside. It's like dirt trapped in an open wound. Ignore it long enough, and the wound will fester and become increasingly more painful. But feelings naturally don't last very long when we just let ourselves feel them. The purpose of finding the feeling is so that you can release it. Feeling the feeling releases the feeling.

All feelings are gentle and short-lived unless there is resistance to feeling the feeling. - **Gay Hendricks**

Feelings are designed to arise and pass away rather quickly. It's when we *resist* them that they get *stuck* and start to cause problems. Resisting the feeling blocks its natural flow.

All feelings serve a positive purpose. They're part of our natural, biological feedback system. So, all feelings are good – even the uncomfortable ones. *Good* feelings feel good. They let us know that all is well. All our needs are being adequately met.

Bad feelings are like alarm bells going off. They're there to alert us whenever there's a threat to our well-being, so we can respond appropriately to restore harmony. The problem is that bad feelings don't feel good. The tendency is to try to avoid feeling them. That never works.

When you put a lid on your bad feelings, it puts a lid on all your feelings. This is the problem with antidepressants. They don't discriminate between good feelings and bad feelings. They put a lid on all feelings. The person may not feel bad anymore, but it comes at the cost of feeling their good feelings. That's no way to live.

This is not an effective strategy for managing emotions. Clients need to know this. Blocking emotions can lead to some very undesirable symptoms because the feelings are still there. They haven't gone anywhere. Repressed feelings just bubble away beneath the surface, building up pressure over time. The solution is to clean house by feeling the feeling.

Many thoughts and feelings were programmed into us early in life so that we could operate at the level of the world. The world, however, is conflicted. Feeling the feeling releases the internal pressure, restoring balance and harmony to the mind-body system. Trust that when balance is restored, healing will happen.

Hippocrates taught that healing isn't something we do. It's something we *allow* by removing the impediments to the natural flow of energy through the body. You can rely on this because cleaning house will result in internal shifts. And when a block has been released, the client will feel it physically. It might come as a sense of relief, or lightness, or peace. They might finally be able to breathe! These are the natural byproducts of releasing.

#3. Carry the Sweepings

Carry the sweepings behind the door is the process of gathering up the positive shifts in perception and feeling by validating them. Putting them behind the door instructs the Subconscious Mind to keep the change. It's a lot like hitting the save button. This encourages the Subconscious to allow more of this change to happen.

Healing tends to be a process of accruing change. It doesn't always happen all at once. This is especially true when you're working with a physical issue because the body is bound to physical laws. That's nature. Emotional change can take time, too, because big emotions are uncomfortable. This can trigger the Subconscious Mind's natural defenses to step in to protect, effectively preventing healing from happening.

Increments of change are much safer and, therefore, easier for the Subconscious Mind to allow. As a result, the client can accrue remarkable changes over time. These incremental changes can then be used to offer tangible proof to the client that they have let something go. You just need to bring attention to it. The client may not realize change is occurring because many of these shifts can seem small, even inconsequential. So, when there's a shift toward the better, bring attention to it. Acknowledge it. Gather it up and set it aside for later.

When learning a skill, don't look for the big, quick improvement. Seek the small improvement one day at a time. - **Daniel Coyle**

The devil understands the secret to true wealth —whether physical, emotional, or spiritual – lies in validating the truth. Instead of trying to suggest change, *validate* each increment of improvement as it occurs. That's the client's truth! Validate any insights or better feelings. Then validate the client's right to continue to grow and change through this process. This paves the way for more change to happen.

As the internal pressure is released, the client will begin to experience more mental clarity. When you're in an event from the past, they'll be able to report more of the details, making your job easier. The client will also begin to experience insights into the cause(s) of the problem and how these things have impacted them in daily life. This opens the door to real change.

Every release produces an increment of change through a shift in perception. This becomes a sweeping that can be set aside as a Subconscious learning. Insight leads to self-understanding and empowerment. Gratitude and compassion begin to flow, allowing forgiveness of self and others. This is when higher states of consciousness can be realized, bringing with them a more expanded sense of fulfillment and wisdom.

Releasing trapped emotions creates a sense of spaciousness in the Mind. Positive emotions flow in to fill that space because positive emotions are aligned with our natural state of health, happiness, and well-being. The space created through the releasing process makes the Subconscious Mind much more receptive to suggestions. Rather than merely offering suggestions for change, offer a *validation* of change immediately following a release. This will reinforce what is already occurring within the client.

Validating what the client is actually experiencing becomes a statement of truth. This will increase suggestibility and encourage learning at a Subconscious level of Mind. You don't need a script for this. All you need to do is validate what is already true for the client. For example, if the client reports that he's feeling better, validate the newer, better feeling.

Validate any insights that may have come to mind. These realizations indicate that learning is occurring. Offer suggestions that validate that change has occurred, is occurring and will continue to occur. Then, validate the client's right to continue to grow and change and improve. Validating increments of change can pave the way for a more dramatic change to happen.

Validating is using the Power of Compounding. Compounding is what happens when you have money in the bank that is earning interest on the interest. Each validation of change is like a brick in the wall of permanent change that you are building.

The first brick begins laying the foundation for subsequent layers of brick. That's the power of one.

1

The bricks are not just stacked on top of one another, however. Proper brick-laying requires that the bricks be staggered to ensure stability. So, the next validation reinforces the primary level by laying another brick down next to the first. This allows the next level to be set in place.

Now there are two bricks on the base with one resting on top, squarely between them. That's the power of three.

$$3$$

$$1 - 2$$

The next validation will, once again, reinforce the energy held in the preceding layers. Another brick is laid on the base, as well as the second level, before establishing the next layer. Now, there are three bricks on the base, two bricks on the second level, and one on top. That's the power of six.

$$6$$

$$3 - 5$$

$$1 - 2 - 4$$

Each validation adds another layer by reinforcing the preceding layers. The next layer will increase the energy of change to ten; four on the base, three on the second layer, two on the third level, and one on the fourth level.

$$10$$

$$6 - 9$$

$$3 - 5 - 8$$

$$1 - 2 - 4 - 7$$

The next layer will be $5 + 4 + 3 + 2 + 1 = 15$ bricks. And so on. Because the power of compounding is exponential, validations of change stack up very quickly in the Subconscious Mind.

All in all, it's just another brick in the wall. - **Pink Floyd**

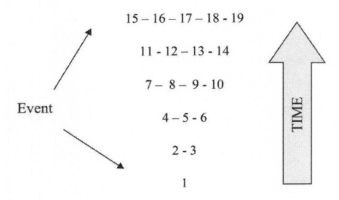

SYMPTOMS EMERGE

15 – 16 – 17 – 18 - 19

11 - 12 – 13 - 14

7 – 8 – 9 - 10

Event   4 – 5 - 6   TIME

2 - 3

1

#4. In General, Keep Order

To keep order means to maintain things in proper relation to one another. This is a task the Subconscious Mind does magnificently. It does so by generalizing all learning. Every sweeping is the by-product of releasing, a small shift in perception that gets set aside, behind the door, as a Subconscious learning. As you stay consistent with the process, these realizations will accrue, and, eventually, the Subconscious Mind will generalize *them* as *truths*.

When a change occurs, it forces the Subconscious Mind into a state of reorganization. It takes these new *learnings* and ripples them throughout the various layers of consciousness, generalizing them to other areas of the person's life. This establishes a new internal level of order and stability. You can encourage the Subconscious Mind's reorganizing efforts by having the client *seal the deal* with a statement of commitment.

First, validate that change is occurring. Then, ask if the client wants to keep these changes. If the client says, "Yes," have them say it out loud. This is called autosuggestion. Autosuggestion is much more powerful than direct suggestion because it's a form of self-talk. The suggestion isn't coming from somebody else. The client is telling this to *themselves*, which, if true, automatically gives the suggestion more weight.

Invite the client to say, "I choose to keep this change." Then, make it reasonable by asking the client to come up with a few *reasons* for holding onto the change. You can do this by using a Sentence Stems Completion exercise. For example, ask the client to say, "I choose to keep this change because [put an ending on it]."

Making it reasonable to accept an increment of change will help to establish an accord between the Conscious Mind, which needs a reason for everything, and the Subconscious Mind, which feels the truth of every thought and decision.

Setting your house in order is essential to liberation. It calls for placing your attention inward to the feeling level of mind, making a clean sweep to eliminate everything you don't want in your consciousness, and then closing the door on it. - **Jason Lotterhand**

Summary

The third step in the set-up phase focuses on testing to ensure that you have a binding Contract, then preparing the client for the work of regression hypnotherapy.

The Contract requires the client to follow instructions and allow uncomfortable emotions to come to the surface of awareness. Hypnosis requires that the client follow instructions. Real regression requires somnambulism. You need to be able to get the client into deep hypnosis very quickly.

Conditioning the client for a rapid induction in the first session can support you in subsequent sessions by allowing you to focus on the client's issue. You can then teach the client how to work with you in a regression session using the 4 Universal Healing Steps.

Learn more in the Create Your Ideal Client Course here: www.tribeofhealers.com/ready-for-regression-first-session-system-course

CHAPTER 7:
4 Universal Healing Steps

Mary presented with a severe fear of snakes. She was perfectly fine so long as no one mentioned the word snake or anything that sounded remotely like snake. This presented an interesting challenge because Mary couldn't actually tell me what her problem was. She couldn't say or write the word snake. We had to play a game of twenty-questions until I could figure out what she was dealing with.

Anything that reminded Mary of snakes would trigger a panic attack. This included the word snack or slither, squiggly lines, and cartoons of snakes. She had a hair-trigger, and when her switch got tripped, the fear would take over.

Mary had been for Cognitive Behavioral Therapy. She had already learned how to cope and avoid any situational triggers. But she still had the problem, and it was controlling her life. Anywhere that there might be snakes was out of bounds for Mary. This included pet stores, zoos, parks, movies, and nature channels on television. Pictures of snakes, whether color or black-and-white, would send her into full-blown panic.

Everyone in her family was walking on eggshells in an attempt to protect Mary and help her to cope. Her son's daycare center had been alerted to eliminate any potential triggers. But something got missed. When Mary was confronted by a small, rubber snake, she had a complete melt-down in front of a group of toddlers. This was the last straw for Mary. That's when she decided to give hypnotherapy a shot.

Snakes were not the problem, however. Mary was walking around with a festering emotional wound from her past that was screaming for healing. This is why the coping strategies weren't working. While she might have managed to adapt to living with the wound, it required her to control everything and everyone around her. It's not possible to control all the externals. There were always going to be unexpected and unavoidable triggers.

Carla presented with a severe case of eczema that covered most of her body. The worst area was her shoulders, where deep lesions cracked and oozed painfully. The itching and pain tormented her night and day. She had tried medication, meditation, psychotherapy, and Brain Balancing Technology. While these had given her some short-term relief, nothing had resolved the problem.

#1. Find it!

The first step in the healing process is to find the feeling and give it permission to come to the surface. It might be a feeling of tension or tightness in the body. It might be an ache or a pain. It might be a lump or a bump. It might be a painful emotion like fear, or anger, or sadness.

Whatever is there, pay attention to it. Honor it. Give it permission to be there. The moment the client gives attention to the feeling, he's no longer avoiding his feelings. As he continues to focus on the feeling, the feeling will get stronger. He'll become more aware of just how uncomfortable that feeling really is. This is how you amplify a feeling. Focus attention on the feelings and sensations in the body.

Just talking about the problem will activate the feeling inside. If you bring their attention to what's happening in the body as they're telling you their Story, they'll find the feeling. Pay attention to what's happening during the intake process because your clients will be going into hypnosis long before you start the formal induction process.

The Subconscious Mind is the emotional Mind, so the moment the client is experiencing an emotion, you have Critical Faculty By-pass. This is a natural induction. The stronger the emotion, the deeper the client will go into the Subconscious Mind. That's hypnosis.

What you're looking for is a targeted feeling in the body. Emotions express as physical sensations in the torso of the body —usually in the throat, the chest, and the gut. The thing to get the client noticing and paying attention to are feelings that are targeted in the body. The clench in the throat. The fist in the gut. The ache in the heart.

In Mary's case, the first step in the healing process was to find the feeling associated with snakes. To elicit this feeling, I used the suggestion, "There's a feeling inside of you that has everything to do with the problem you're seeing me about." Notice I didn't mention snakes? Mary's Conscious and Subconscious Minds both knew what I was referring to, but saying the word snake would have triggered a strong abreaction. It was too soon for that. At this stage of the process,

Mary needed to learn that it was safe to allow feelings and emotions to come to conscious awareness.

Carla found a feeling of fear in her gut. This wasn't the only feeling tormenting Carla, but fear is the mother of all negative emotions. That's always a good place to begin. Focus on the fear because fear is a feeling that says, *Something bad might happen.* That fear is learned. It's an expectation that has roots in a past experience. In Carla's case, the fear was rooted in a deep hurt that had occurred in infancy.

Every symptom is the result of a life experience. This is the fundamental basis of regression-to-cause hypnosis. So, the first step is to find the feeling because that's coming out of the event of wounding. The place to find a feeling is in the body. That's where we feel our feelings. Once you find a feeling, you can choose to either release the feeling or follow it back to its source. What you decide will depend on the client's readiness for regression.

The goal of regression hypnotherapy is to locate the causal event and resolve the problem where it got started. But to locate the causal event, you need a strong signal. A weak signal will fizzle out before you get there. That can be frustrating. So, the client must be ready, willing, and able to allow uncomfortable feelings to come to full awareness.

To bridge back to the causal event, you need to find an actual emotion like fear, anger, or sadness. Subtle or vague sensations in the body are not specific or strong enough to make the connection to the event of wounding. A feeling like anxiety is distributed throughout the body. It's too vague to provide an effective bridge. Emotions, on the other hand, are targeted feelings in the torso. i.e., gut, chest, throat.

To find the feeling, suggest to the client that there is an uncomfortable feeling inside that has everything to do with the problem they are seeing you about. This will provoke the feeling to come out of its hidey-hole. Then, bring attention to what's happening in the body.

Remember, emotions don't just come out of nowhere. They're based on actual life experiences that made strong impressions. There's nothing happening in your office to cause that feeling. "That feeling" is trapped inside, hidden within an unresolved event from the past. That's what's in the cauldrons in hell – memories.

What's keeping that memory alive is the energy of the event. That's the fire. So, focus attention on the emotion. That knot in the gut is Subconscious communication. What emotion might it be? That clench in the throat or the chest is a signal from the past. Encourage the client to name that emotion. Fear? Anger? Sadness? Something else?

Having the client focus their full attention on the feeling in the body will amplify the feeling, giving you a stronger bridge to the causal event. Naming the feeling will give you a targeted signal to follow. So, give that feeling permission to be there.

Teach the client to honor their Subconscious Mind by allowing feelings to be acknowledged and felt because, when the client is connecting to an emotion physically, they're *already* beginning to regress. The event that's responsible for that feeling is coming to the surface of awareness.

The event is right there, in the memory pot. So, the client doesn't travel back in time. Their Conscious Mind steps *into* the feeling that's still stuck in the past event. That's essentially all there is to regression. Regression is a journey without distance because, as far as the Subconscious Mind is concerned, it's all happening now.

The only place a feeling can hurt us is trapped inside. Unfortunately, uncomfortable feelings are like dirt trapped in an open wound. Ignore them long enough, and the wound will fester. We need to clean the wound. The way to clean the wound is to feel the feeling that's trapped in the body's energy system.

#2. Feel it!

Mary was dealing with a big, hairy-scary fear of snakes. I taught Mary how to allow just enough of the feeling to come up so that she could release it. This taught her that she didn't have to avoid the feeling, nothing bad was going to happen if she just let herself feel the feeling, and I wasn't going to dump her into a snake pit. As a result, she discovered that it was possible for her to feel better.

This gave her the confidence she needed to trust me to guide the healing process. Through the process, the feeling of fear took us back to Mary's childhood, where we discovered the truth. Snakes weren't the problem. Her brother was the problem! It seems that her older brother had taken to bullying Mary from a tender, young age.

Mary was a sensitive child, to begin with, and the bullying continued well into her teens. This created an internal conflict. Mary loved her brother. She also feared him. Love and fear cannot occupy the same space, so this was the underlying conflict. When Mary's brother took advantage of the opportunity to torment his little sister by taunting her with a snake, her Subconscious Mind came up with the perfect solution. All the unresolved feelings trapped inside got transferred onto snakes.

Mary's fear of snakes was a brilliant Subconscious solution to a much deeper issue. Mary wasn't safe. Mary was an especially sensitive child, so her parents brushed aside her fear, refusing to take her seriously when she tattled on her brother. Instead of protecting Mary, they took the "boys will be boys" stance, leaving Mary vulnerable and afraid.

As an adult, Mary could distance herself from her abusive brother. (In fact, she moved half-way across the country to do so!) But every time Mary saw her brother, the irrational fears of childhood got triggered. And in the absence of her brother, there were always snakes.

Snakes acted as surrogates, reminding her of her abusive brother and just how vulnerable she was as a child. And the fear just kept getting stronger. Anger got added to the mix. Anger toward her brother's cruelty. Anger towards her parent's inability to see how scared she was. Hurt at how they had abandoned her. She also blamed herself. She wasn't normal. She wasn't like other people. She was terrified that her son would inherit her dis-ease.

Releasing the many layers of accumulated emotions of a lifetime took some time. We had to proceed slowly and gently. Safety is Rule #1. But Mary reclaimed her power and ability to feel safe again. She forgave the people who had had let her down, transforming her relationships with family members.

In time, Mary no longer felt the need to avoid snakes. She realized that she didn't have to like snakes, but they were not an actual threat to her life. This set her free from the past.

On one occasion, she attended a garden party (a potentially hazardous situation in the past). When one of the children ran up behind her and waved a small snake in front of her face, Mary didn't even flinch, much to the surprise of her family. Mary now truly understood that she didn't have to go through life, feeling afraid all the time. At long last, she was free to enjoy life.

The most important person in a child's life is the primary caregiver. Usually, that's Mom. A child is dependent upon caregivers for survival. Regardless of the circumstances that resulted in a client's issue, Mom is often a factor, either for what she did or failed to do. Carla's feelings went back to infancy.

The initial wounding event had to do with being rejected by her mother at birth. Carla, it seems, was the result of an unwanted pregnancy. Being rejected by her mother planted the seeds of fear in Carla. Every infant knows that it needs to be taken care of. If the child is abandoned, it will die. So, Carla was literally in fear for her life.

While she was dutifully fed and changed, as required, she was abandoned physically and emotionally. Baby Carla was left alone for long hours, not knowing if anyone would ever come! While Carla's physical needs were met, her emotional needs during her developmental years were seriously neglected.

Carla's only saving grace was that her father adored her, but he was absent for most of the day. As she grew older, Carla tried desperately to gain her mother's love and approval, to no avail. Over time, Carla's deep hurt turned to hatred toward her mother. She blamed herself for being a burden. This belief created blocks around money.

Every problem you deal with will have roots in some kind of stress. Remember, stress is a natural, biological response to the perception of threat, whether real or imagined. This causes the body to produce stress hormones to facilitate fighting or fleeing. Meanwhile, other functions not directly necessary to survive are put on hold. These include growth, reproduction, immune, and skin functions, as well as cognition. Once trapped feelings are given permission to express, they can be released fully, and healing will happen.

Carla let herself feel the truth of her feelings. She released the emotional pain that her skin had been trying to express. She found forgiveness for Mom and herself. Miraculously, her skin problem healed completely without the need for medications. As a happy side-benefit, Carla also released 10 pounds of excess weight effortlessly, and her money problems evaporated!

We never treated Carla's symptoms. The skin problem, the weight problem, and the money problem weren't the problem. They were symptoms, tangible evidence of an underlying, unresolved problem at a Subconscious level of Mind. By finding the feeling, we were able to follow the feeling to its source. This gave us access to the symptom-requiring problem – a life experience. Resolving the real problem resulted in *real* healing and the symptoms dissolved away on their own.

Releasing Techniques

Feeling the feeling releases the feeling. Emotions want to move. Emotion. Incorporating some sort of movement will help to facilitate a quicker and deeper releasing of the feeling. For example, Pillow Therapy, which is the traditional approach to release anger as part of the forgiveness work, involves physical movement. The pumping action gets the feeling moving in the body.

Another approach to releasing uncomfortable thoughts and emotions is Meridian Tapping Techniques (MTT). MTT is the umbrella term for all energy-psychology modalities such as Thought Field Therapy (TFT) and Emotional Freedom Technique (EFT). There are many variations and versions to choose from. They all work and are very easy to apply in hypnosis.

There's some debate on how tapping works, and no one knows for sure. Some believe it has to do with our biology. Others believe that tapping works to interrupt trauma patterns. Many believe our energy field interacts with our physiology and that tapping works to release the negative emotions associated with painful, historical events. Dr.

Bruce Lipton, the author of *The Biology of Belief,* refers to energy psychology as" a burgeoning field based in the New Biology" that promises to change our genetic programming.

From an energy-psychology perspective, tapping on the points accesses the key meridian pathways to release blocks from the nervous system of the body. As trapped energy is freed to flow through and be expressed, the client will experience relief. Often, very quickly.

Dr. Robert Scaer, author of *The Body Bears the Burden,* is an expert in the field of trauma. Because of the way the brain processes information, Scaer sees great promise in tapping as a therapeutic modality in the field of somatic psychology.

Regression hypnotherapy involves the search for the causal event as well as subsequent events that served to reinforce the Initial Sensitizing Event (ISE). In brain theory, the ISE is the event that caused the amygdala to become hypersensitive (sensitized) to that specific stimulus. The amygdala is the part of the brain responsible for fear conditioning. It's the early warning system in the emotional brain that processes perceptions of threat.

When the amygdala gets stimulated repeatedly, it results in sensitization to the trigger (i.e., classical conditioning). Dr. Scaer cites the case of a woman whose amygdala was calcified. As a result, she couldn't feel fear or rage. She was completely placid. It seems that without the amygdala-arousal, we are incapable of feeling fear or anger. So, the key to resolving those feelings is to turn down the amygdala.

One of the things that will turn down the amygdala is *social bonding*. In indigenous societies, people heal through ritual. If you use a ritual that's acceptable, it will tend to inhibit the amygdala. Dr. Scaer states, "Because EFT is associated with a lot of ritual, whether or not the tapping on the meridian planes and points is homeostatic, regulating the autonomic nervous system, or whether its ritual, probably isn't important. It is probably both."

Another way to turn down the amygdale is through *empowerment*. The tapping phrases, while they may sound mechanistic and trivial, are actually statements of empowerment. Tapping provides both social bonding and empowerment, which calms the amygdala while focusing on the trigger, effectively extinguishing trauma.

Meridian Tapping Techniques

Roger Callahan, the developer of Thought Field Therapy (TFT), believed that each emotion or problem required diagnosis and treatment with a specific algorithm, tapping on a sequence of points. The problem with this approach is that sometimes there are multiple and/or conflicting emotions, and it is not always possible to differentiate one emotion from another. While Callahan sought to establish that tapping alone would affect a cure, and certainly there is evidence to support this, it can take many treatments to address the many aspects contributing to a client's problem.

There are those who have gone beyond Callahan's methods to discover that the use of suggestion improves the results and that the algorithms are not so important. Gary Craig, the developer of Emotional Freedom Techniques (EFT), felt that specific algorithms were unnecessary and developed a basic *recipe* that could be applied to any issue. He believed that EFT could become a universal healing aid.

EFT has proven to be very effective in removing negative emotions, reducing food cravings, reducing or eliminating pain, and implementing positive goals. Craig continues to challenge us to try it on everything. By providing a free manual and a comprehensive library of case studies for anyone who wants it, Gary Craig has given the world a powerful drug-free, cost-effective, self-help tool that anyone can use.

The cause of all negative emotions is a disruption in the body's energy system. - **Gary Craig**

Steve Wells and Dr. David Lake, creators of Provocative Energy Techniques, found that a person can tap in any sequence, and, so long as they are focusing attention, they will still get results. In fact, anyone can learn how to do it in just a few minutes. Whatever tapping is, research has shown that it affects the deep Subconscious. That's where we work. Tapping is a wonderful tool to add to your healing kit.

Tapping is a ritual that utilizes things like repetition, auto-suggestion, and focused concentration – all components of hypnosis. This makes it a natural hypnotic induction. Because it seems like you're just talking, the client isn't on the alert for the beginning of hypnosis. And in the absence of any resistance to entering the state, it just happens. Tapping can be used as a Covert Induction.

Tapping keeps the Conscious Mind occupied by giving it more than one thing to do at a time. Simultaneously moving through the tapping sequence, paying attention to sensations in the body, speaking the statements, and noticing associations that arise during the process overloads the conscious, thinking mind. This makes tapping a Confusional Induction technique, as well.

Most clients will enter into a light state of hypnosis while tapping. As soon as a strong emotion comes to the surface of awareness, realize that you have Critical Faculty By-pass (CFB). And the stronger the emotion is, the deeper the hypnosis. You can use tapping to get a client into a very state of deep hypnosis.

Not every client will not be ready for regression immediately. Some clients need more time to be prepared for the process. In this case, preliminary techniques like tapping can be used to prepare a client for the work of regression hypnotherapy. If you teach tapping to the client in the first session, you will amaze your clients with how quickly they can find relief. This makes it an effective Convincer. It only takes a few rounds for the client to master the technique. And it soon becomes automatic for the client to close their eyes and focus inward while tapping. You can then use it in your regression sessions as an induction and to release uncomfortable feelings and emotions that got trapped in past events.

#3. Heal it!

Healing happens when we let it. This is something Hippocrates taught. Healing isn't something we do. It's something we *allow* to happen by removing the impediments to the natural flow of energy through the body. When a block has been released, the client will feel it physically as a sense of relief, lightness, or peace. To the client, this is tangible evidence that something has been let go. As a result, the benefits of releasing internal stress can be obtained organically through the process.

a) Physically – feeling better; feelings of relief, safety, security, calm, peacefulness, and relaxation.
b) Mentally – increased clarity. As the client is able to think more clearly, the mind begins to connect the dots between cause and effect.
c) Emotionally – Insight leads to understanding, which allows feelings of empowerment and compassion.
d) Spiritually – Empowerment and compassion allow forgiveness of self and others, resulting in wisdom and gratitude.

Small internal shifts can turn out to be giant leaps in terms of healing because once accepted, the Subconscious Mind will naturally generalize all change. Once a change has been recognized, no matter how small, the next step is to encourage the Subconscious Mind to integrate it at a deeper level.

The way to do this is to bring the client's attention to the fact there has been a shift and validate it. The client may not always realize when a change has occurred. Your job is to bring it to mind by guiding the client to notice that something has shifted internally.

How can they know they have released something? They'll feel it! A better feeling will rush in to replace the uncomfortable feeling. So, when something has changed, even a little, validate that change. Celebrate it as if you've just won the lottery! This encourages the Subconscious Mind to allow more change to happen, which will make your job easier.

Validating small changes as they occur makes it safer and easier for the client to allow bigger changes to occur. Big changes are often seen as a threat. It's too much of a leap into the unknown. It doesn't seem possible. This can generate resistance. But even a small shift for the better can change the client's overall trajectory in life. That's all you need.

The journey of a thousand miles begins with a single step. - **Chinese Proverb**

Healing is seldom a one-time event. It's a journey. One small step naturally leads to a shift toward the better, which allows the next step, and then the next. In this way, the client can accrue the benefits of change. It's maybe a single step, but it's one step closer toward the client's ultimate goal of healing. Encourage and reinforce positive changes by using statements of validation, recognition, and appreciation with either direct or auto-suggestion.

Validating any change can generate insight. Insight is a form of self-knowledge. It's a moment of realization, where something that was not consciously recognized before is brought to light, a moment of enlightenment. This new awareness changes the client because they are discovering something about themselves that they didn't know before. So, keep good notes because this is gold! You can use it to formulate powerful suggestions later!

Once you have found the feeling, you can choose to either release it or follow it back to the event of wounding. The easiest place to do the releasing work is in the causal event because you don't have to deal with an accumulative effect of reinforcing events over time. Once you have cleansed the wound, the client will feel calm and a sense of peace, indicating they are in a state of high receptivity. This is the time to apply healing suggestions that validate change because healing is happening. Encourage it! Then, seal in all the changes.

#4. Seal it!

The final Universal Healing step is a protective measure to ensure the client will hold onto the changes that are occurring. It's like hitting the save button on all the positive changes. To seal means to lock in. This is the purpose of your session wrap-up. It's to seal in all the changes that have occurred, encourage a deeper level of healing, and ensure that the results will be lasting.

This final step makes use of preliminary testing techniques and surface techniques. Preliminary testing techniques such as future pacing and mental rehearsal allow you to make sure that you got everything and that the healing is complete. Surface techniques such as guided imagery and direct suggestion can then be used to reinforce and generalize all the positive changes that have occurred.

Begin with a quick review of whatever happened during the session. What did the client discover? What insights were brought to light? How much better do they feel as a result of having let something go? What other changes are now possible because of having made these changes?

Tie all these things to the client's Therapeutic Goal. How will these realizations, shifts toward the better, and insights contribute to achieving their goal? Remind the client of all the desired benefits of change. That's the motivating factor. This will keep them committed to achieving a complete resolution of the problem.

Summary

The 4 Universal Healing Steps can be applied to every phase of the healing process. Where you will find them most useful is while facilitating the emotional release work. Releasing techniques that are highly effective in regression hypnotherapy sessions include tapping and Pillow Therapy.

Not every client will not be ready for regression immediately. Some clients need more time to be prepared for the process. Teaching your clients how to release a feeling before you begin the regression process can help to prepare the client for the healing process, giving you a much better client to work with.

1. Find it – focus attention on the feeling.
2. Feel it – feel the feeling to release it.
3. Heal it – validate increments of improvement and compound change.
4. Seal it – elicit a commitment to keep the change.

Learn more in the Create Your Ideal Client Course here: www.tribeofhealers.com/ready-for-regression-first-session-system-course

I will use treatment to help the sick. I will never use it to injure them or wrong them. I will not give poison to anyone. — **The Hippocratic Oath**

CHAPTER 8:
Emotional Release Work

The causal event is like an infected, open wound. What makes it so painful is that the toxic emotions trapped inside the event create internal pressure. Releasing the trapped emotions relieves the internal pressure, which brings the client relief. Release everything and the energy trapped in the event of wounding can be directed toward healing.

The key to healing is to release the feeling. The way to release a feeling is to feel it. There are many ways to do this, but the most common emotional-release techniques used in regression hypnotherapy sessions are talking, tapping, and Pillow Therapy. Meridian Tapping Techniques (MTT) entails a very simple process that can easily be incorporated into your regression sessions to release uncomfortable emotions.

#1. Find it!

Focus on what bothers you (the more specific, the better the results)

I often teach tapping to the client in the first session. During the intake and educational pre-talk, I wait and watch for an emotion to surface. When it happens, I then bring the client's attention to:

1. What sensations are they're feeling in the body?
2. Where in the body is that feeling is being expressed?
3. What specific emotion might that feeling be?
4. How uncomfortable is that feeling on a scale of 1 – 10?
5. Do they want to hold onto that feeling or release it?

This is how you set up for the releasing work. Once you have the client focused on the feeling, with their permission, you can then teach the client how to release a feeling. I like to begin with tapping because anyone can learn how to do it in just a few minutes. There's really no right or wrong way to do it. And it can prove to the client that they can feel better very quickly.

#2. Feel it!

Tapping helps keeps the client focused on the *feeling*. Feeling the feeling releases it. This is how you will clean house. While focusing on the feeling associated with the issue while applying a sequence of touching, tapping, or rubbing.

Keep the focus on the body while thinking about the problem. The key is to be as specific as possible. E.g., *This tight knot in my gut. This scared feeling in my throat.* Talking and tapping work beautifully together. So, it's easy to incorporate into the intake or pre-talk phases of the process.

Teach the client how to use auto-suggestion and tapping to acknowledge and release uncomfortable emotions. E.g., *I feel scared! I can feel it in my gut!* That's the truth. And truth-telling is good for the soul. It's like giving a confession. This teaches the client that it's okay to admit some (awful) truth. They won't die, and you won't judge them. This is setting up for the uncovering procedure of regression hypnotherapy.

This is working *with* the Subconscious Mind. The *feeling* isn't the problem. It's the Subconscious Mind's way of saying, *Help! There's a problem here!* So, we want to honor that. The real problem has to do with the event that *caused* the feeling. That's where we want to go. But to gain permission to go *there*, you need to prove that it's safe for feelings to come to consciousness to be released.

The Tapping Sequence

The following is the traditional tapping sequence, but the actual sequence you use doesn't seem to matter so long as you include at least three to four different points in the process. Tap, don't pound. Use the same pressure you would use if you were tapping on the arm of the chair.

1. Inside of eyebrow (IE)
2. Side of eye (SE)
3. Under eye (UE)
4. Under nose (UN)
5. Under lip (UL)
6. Collar bone (CB)
7. Breast bone/thymus
8. Thumbnail
9. Index finger
10. Middle finger
11. Pinkie

12. Karate Chop (KC)

Other Points You Can Tap On:

- Under arm (UA)

- Top of head (TH)

- Inside wrists (IW)

Begin the tapping sequence with the Karate Chop Point (KC) or rubbing the Sore Spot (SS) and repeating the Basic Self-Acceptance Phrase three times. "Even though I have this [insert negative perception/feeling] . . . I deeply and completely accept myself anyway."

Proceed through the Tapping Sequence while repeating a Reminder Phrase. "This [insert feeling, descriptor, and body location]." For example, this tight, angry feeling in my gut.

Tap on each point five to seven times each while repeating the Reminder Phrase. The purpose of the reminder phrase is to keep the focus on the feeling. The more specific you can be, the better your outcomes will be.

Finish each sequence on the Karate Chop Point (KC) and the self-acceptance phrase. "And I deeply and completely accept myself." Then, have the client take a deep breath, exhale, and go inside to notice what, if anything, is left.

If the client still has some discomfort, take a SUD. SUD stands for Subjective Unit of Discomfort. Just have the client rate the intensity of the feeling on a scale of 1 – 10. Then, compare it to where it was at when you started by taking a retroactive SUD. For example, the client states the feeling is a six, ask, "How strong was that feeling when we started?"

If the feeling was stronger to begin with (e.g., 10), then you know that some of it has been released. You just need to continue releasing until it's all gone. To release what remains, modify the set-up phrase to "Even though I still feel some of this [insert feeling descriptor], I deeply and completely accept myself."

Change the reminder phrase as you tap the points to "This remaining [insert feeling descriptor]."

If the feeling hasn't changed, you either need to . . .

1. Increase focus on the feeling, or
2. Get more specific with your suggestions.

Remember, feeling the feeling is what releases the feeling. To increase the focus of attention on the feeling, ask the client to describe the feeling. How big is it? Does it have a color? Does it have a shape, a temperature? The more specific you can be, the better your results will be.

The language of the Subconscious Mind is image and emotion. What specific emotion might that feeling be? Sad? Angry? Scared? Something else? If it could speak, what would it say? Give the feeling permission to speak by saying, "I feel [put an ending on it]."

Pillow Therapy

The trick to releasing is to match your technique to the client's level of discomfort. Tapping can be used to release pretty much anything. But when a client brings to awareness something that is very tender, change your approach to match the energy of the feeling. Child Parts are feelings Parts. Pay attention to the client's tone of voice. Often, there will be a shift because the client has regressed to a younger age. When this happens, realize that you're dealing with an Inner Child and shift to a more maternal approach. Encourage the client to let the feeling flow.

Sometimes I will tap very gently and slowly on the points *for* the client. This allows the client to focus fully on the feeling. When tears run down the client's cheek and neck, I gently dab them with a tissue. This loving gesture encourages the release of sadness and grief and provides much-needed support to the wounded Inner Child. Big, hairy scary feelings, on the other hand, can come on too strong, putting the client into a state of overwhelm. When intense emotions like terror or rage come to the surface of awareness, it can be very frightening for the client. There's too much volume and intensity!

If the client reports a feeling of panic, get out your pillow. If the client can't breathe, they may not be able to speak. Don't leave them stuck in the feeling! Take charge, get out your pillow, and direct the client to pump the feeling into the pillow. Pillow Work can provide faster relief than tapping or talking.

Gently place a pillow on the client's lap, and instruct them to "Stay focused on that feeling." Then, show them how to release the feeling by taking their hand and forming it into a fist. Then, pump it up and down a few times into the pillow while giving the suggestion to get it out. Let the client know that what they're doing is giving the feeling a place to go. This means that they won't have to carry it around inside anymore.

Getting it out will help the client to feel better very quickly. Tell them, "You get that out, you're going to feel sooooooo good. Now, get it out! You get it all out, and it's over!" Calm support and allowing the feeling to move will help to restore balance very quickly.

Really BIG feelings like anger move out much more quickly if the client turns up the volume and uses bigger movements. Shouting is highly effective when you're dealing with a loud emotion like anger and can be especially empowering for female clients. Just make it clear that what you're asking them to do is *pump* the feeling out of the body, and into the pillow, as a way to feel better. The client mustn't ever interpret this approach as *hitting*. Any association to violence can bring up strong resistance. We want to give that feeling in the gut or the throat a place to go. That's the pillow.

It's truly amazing how quickly helping a client to release the internal pressure can restore balance to the mind-body system. Not only will this help the client to feel more in control of how they feel, it will give you a much more cooperative client when it comes to facilitating the healing processes of regression hypnotherapy.

#3. Heal it!

Notice what has changed as a result of the process.

Healing happens very naturally, given the right conditions. Releasing uncomfortable thoughts and feeling creates the conditions for healing to happen. All you need to do is bring attention to every shift toward the better and validate it. The way to do this is to complete a round of releasing. Then test.

Following a round of tapping or pillow purging, give the client a moment to rest and recalibrate. Then, have them go inside and notice what's changed. Most of the time, the client is going to be feeling better. But they may not realize this until you instruct them to go inside and notice.

If the client says, "I feel better!" validate it. Say, "Good job!" or "Nicely done!" Then, invite the client to say it out loud, "I feel better!" Turn it into a revelation by adding, "I'm allowed to feel better!"

Seriously, too many people don't know that they're allowed to feel their feelings. Your job is to validate feelings and emotions because this is how the Subconscious Mind communicates. Whatever is there, allowing it to express is good.

If the client says, "I still feel (scared)," it just means that they haven't completely released the feeling. Take a SUD. How much of the feeling has been released? Validate that. Then, release on whatever is left.

The goal is to get a complete releasing by bringing the SUD level down to zero. Statements of validation encourage the Subconscious Mind to allow more of the feeling to come to awareness to be released. For example, if that tight, choking feeling of fear in the throat was a 10, and now it's down to a 5, that's a 50% improvement in just a few minutes! Point that out!

Human beings naturally have a negative bias. The tendency is to focus on the discomfort. But change tends not to happen all at once. If the client is stuck in all or nothing thinking, they're going to overlook the fact that the energy is moving. Validating increments of improvement can get the client moving in the right direction.

Bring awareness to the process of *change* as it is occurring by validating every change for the better. If something still remains, validate that, too. For example, *Even though I still have some of that scared feeling in my throat, I do feel better.* I'm allowed to feel better! Then, continue with the process of releasing.

Find the feeling, feel the feeling. Wash, rinse, repeat. Remember, we're cleaning house. That means everything, unlike love, must go! If it doesn't feel good, it doesn't need to be there. It can be recognized, felt, and released completely, allowing the client to feel good again. Say to the client, "Take a deep breath and exhale. As you exhale, go inside and just notice what's changed."

Acknowledge it. Validate it! Celebrate it! Realize, you got your energy moving!

#4. Seal it!

Once the client has released all the internal pressure, they'll be feeling calmer, more relaxed, and at peace. In this state, the Mind becomes highly receptive to suggestions for change. This is the perfect time to pour in a few suggestions that are aligned with the client's internal experience.

Use suggestions to compound what is already true, and your suggestion will go in like a hot knife through butter. You don't need a script. Just reinforce the insights and changes that have already occurred and trust the Subconscious Mind to do what it was designed to do — heal!

Summary

The key to healing is in the Emotional Release Work. Releasing the internal pressure brings the client rapid relief. Two techniques that lend themselves equally well to regression hypnotherapy are tapping (EFT) and Pillow Therapy.

While tapping is effective for virtually any feeling, the larger movements associated with pumping into a pillow make it easier to release bigger emotions like anger.

Emotional Release Work follows the 4 Universal Healing Steps.

1. Find it – Find the feeling in the body.
2. Feel it – Release the feeling by tapping or pumping it into a pillow.
3. Heal it – Notice what has changed and validate it.
4. Seal it – Offer suggestions to compound change.

CHAPTER 9:
Don't Look

"**B**ut," said the Devil, "don't look into those caldrons! Not even once, or you'll be in trouble." The soldier said that he understood and promised everything would be all right. And the devil went off on his travels, leaving the soldier to take up his duties tending the fire, sweeping, carrying the sweepings behind the back door - everything just as he'd been instructed.

"Don't look" means don't try to remember. Don't think. Don't analyze. Don't judge. Just stay focused on the feeling and let the Subconscious Mind reveal the way out of the problem. Remember, regression happens. It's natural. You just need to make it safe for the client to go where you need them to go and do what you need them to do to secure healing.

Some clients will be ready to dive right into the regression work. Others are going to be highly resistant to uncomfortable feelings. Most are going to need a little persuading before they're willing to participate fully in finding, feeling, and releasing uncomfortable emotions. Don't ask a client to go *there* until you're sure that they're ready.

1. A client is ready for regression when they can:
2. Follow instructions to achieve a state of somnambulism.
3. Is convinced that the hypnosis happened.
4. Is willing to allow uncomfortable feelings and emotions to come to conscious awareness.
5. Is able to release uncomfortable feelings and emotions to feel better.

The client does the work.

All healing is self-healing. You just can't do it for the client. The client must be prepared to do the work necessary to get the results. To heal it, the client must be prepared to face it and feel it. That means things are going to get uncomfortable. But human beings are hardwired to seek pleasure and avoid pain. Nobody wants to feel uncomfortable.

The real problem is a Pain Story that the Conscious Mind doesn't know about, can't fix, or doesn't want to look at. The Subconscious Mind is duty-bound to protect. One of the ways it does this is by protecting the client from painful memories. The devil knows better than to take the lid off painful past events right away.

There's a lid on those cauldrons for a reason! And nothing is going to happen until the Subconscious Mind feels that it's safe to *let* it happen. Trapped inside each cauldron is a memory of an event, bubbling and boiling with unresolved, uncomfortable feelings and emotions from the past. The lid is there to protect by keeping all the details of a past event hidden from consciousness. Taking the lid off too soon can cause problems.

You don't need problems. You need a real regression back to the causal event. You need the client to be able to step into an event from the past and revivify the experience. You need them to be seeing, hearing, smelling, tasting and feeling it, not merely remembering the experience.

This is what makes regression to cause hypnosis different from other approaches. Hypnotic methods such as dissociation or suggesting away an emotion attempt to protect the client from the contents of their own Mind. Avoiding what's causing the problem won't get the client healed.

The purpose of dissociation is to prevent the unconscious from becoming conscious. In times of crisis, this can be helpful by offering short-term relief. Anti-depressants can be helpful. Dissociation techniques can be helpful. But for long-term relief, you need to find out what's causing the problem.

If you're dealing with an emotional issue, the dissociated point of view won't give you access to all the details. And trying to protect a person from their feelings only reinforces the problem of avoidance. Worse, merely treating the symptoms eventually leads to a recurrence, recidivism, or conversion.

Recurrence, Recidivism, Conversion

When you're dealing with an emotional issue, the symptom is seldom the whole problem. It's a Subconscious Solution to the real problem. If you try to remove the symptom without addressing the underlying cause, the symptom will either recur or express in a different way.

Symptom recurrence is what happens when you only treat the symptom. Treatment resolves the lump, bump, ache, pain or rash, temporarily. But eventually, the symptoms reappear, requiring further treatment. Why? Because the symptom is not the problem. It's Subconscious communication pointing to a deeper issue.

Recidivism is what happens when you only treat the behavior. The relapse rate for conventional approaches to treating alcoholism is 40% - 60%. Smokers have a 60% - 90% relapse rate in the first year. Ninety percent of dieters who successfully lose weight will regain it, and then some, within two years. Why? Because eating, smoking, or drinking are not the problem. They are Subconscious Solutions to a deeper problem.

Symptom Conversion is what happens when the Subconscious Mind comes up with a better solution to the problem. It might take the form of a new symptom or move to a new location. For example, physical pain will jump to another part of the body. So, if you find yourself chasing a physical pain around the body, you're probably dealing with an emotional issue.

The Subconscious Mind can't tell the difference between physical pain and emotional pain. Both are processed by the same area of the brain. This is why depression hurts physically. If you block the pain with drugs or hypnotic suggestion, you are turning off the Subconscious Mind's only way of communicating. It starts looking for a different solution. Usually, it will come up with something that is harder to get rid of.

This is why surface approaches fail. It's why people who quit smoking often gain weight. It's why the rate of recidivism with drug and alcohol abuse is so high and why a high percentage of criminals re-offend. It's because the emotion driving the need to smoke or drink, overeat, gamble or rape hasn't been resolved.

Too many hypnosis practitioners only deal with symptoms. They think that the behavior is the problem, or the pain is the problem, and their focus is on getting rid of *that*. But trying to suggest away an emotional issue is like telling the Subconscious Mind to shut up. That's not a good idea.

Worse, sometimes, a simple technique will actually work. But very few hypnotherapists actually track their results over time. If there happens to be a recurrence some time down the road, they'll never know. And when that happens, the client will assume that the hypnosis didn't work.

The problem is that you can't use a surface technique on a deeper issue and expect to get a *lasting* result. To get a lasting result, you need to get to the root of the problem. You need to dig down beneath the surface, pull out all the roots, and make sure that you get everything that's feeding into the problem.

The underlying emotion might be a feeling of fear, or sadness, or anger, or something else, but behind every unhappy emotion is an unmet need. The feeling isn't the problem. It's the Subconscious Mind waving a red flag and yelling, "Hey! Look over here!" The emotion is a Subconscious signal telling you *where* to look because it's coming out of the event that caused it.

Complexity

Some issues are relatively simple. They have a kind of linearity to them. In this case, there will be a direct path leading from where the client is now into the causal event. There will be only a few events feeding into the issue. And only one emotion to deal with.

This is the simple regression model most of us were taught in hypnosis school. But in real life, clients don't come in textbooks. Because problems tend to develop over time, more stuff can get added to the initial problem, adding complexity. There can be multiple events; multiple aspects; multiple layers of perceptions, thoughts, and feelings; and more than one causal event contributing to a problem.

Your approach is always going to be the same. But the more stuff there is calling for resolution, the more time it will take to get complete healing. And when you're dealing with traumatic memories, there's going to be a significant emotional charge trapped in the event. This is what holds the memory in place.

What makes any event memorable has to do with the feeling. The problem is that the Subconscious Mind doesn't keep time the same way as the Conscious Mind. The Conscious Mind organizes events along a linear timeline and creates stories as a way to make sense of those experiences. This provides a much-needed sense of control.

I overeat because . . . I'm afraid of spiders because . . . That's the Conscious Mind coming up with a Story that makes sense of things. But the Subconscious Mind doesn't work that way. When an event is left unresolved, it doesn't get stored as a past event. It gets held onto so the Subconscious Mind can keep working on it.

It's still active as a situation of concern. The Subconscious Mind keeps trying to come up with a solution, but it can't because it only has the resources that were available at that time. If the event occurred in childhood, it only has the resources of a Child. This is why Inner Child

Work is so central to regression hypnotherapy. Most of the time, you're going to be going back into childhood because the younger the child is, the more impressionable they are. And the more vulnerable they are to any perceived threat. That, by definition, is trauma.

Trauma

Trauma has been defined as "the perception of a threat while in a state of helplessness." It's about feeling vulnerable. Every Child is helpless. So, everyone has experienced some kind of childhood trauma.

Problems arise when an experience doesn't end well. When a traumatic experience doesn't get dealt with and resolved right away, it gets held over as a current event. This means that, Subconsciously, the threat is still present. Most of the time, it turns out that what was happening was misinterpreted by the child. But when the problem is left unresolved, it gets carried over into adulthood and continues to generate the seemingly irrational fears of the Child.

This is what we often find in regression sessions. The threat was, in reality, no big deal. It's just that the Child lacked the information or the maturity to be able to make sense of what was happening. As a result, it felt overwhelming for the Child. This is what the Subconscious Mind is trying to protect the client from. It's the threat of being overwhelmed again.

The Subconscious Mind doesn't know that the client is an adult because the Child is still stuck in that event, trying to find a way out. Subconsciously, there's still a threat. To protect the Child, the Subconscious Mind will prevent the memory from being brought to conscious awareness. Your job is to work *with* the Subconscious Mind by protecting the client as you guide them through the process.

You need to make it safe for the client to allow their deepest feelings to come to the surface. You need them to trust you to guide them so that they'll go where you need them to go and do what you need them to do when you ask them to. If you don't, you're going to have to deal with resistance.

If you make it safe for the client to follow your instructions, when it comes time to do the regression, it will happen very easily. One of the ways that you can set up for it to happen easily is to use a positive regression in the first session. Don't look in the pots. Just take the client back into pleasant, comfortable, happy events in the past.

There's no resistance to going back to happier times. And while you're there, you can train your star athlete! You can use the safety of a positive regression to uncover resources that can support the client in healing. You can introduce many of the tools and techniques you will be using together and assess the client's readiness for regression before you start looking in the pots.

Not only will this make your job easier, but it will also give you a better client to work with when you start guiding them into rough terrain. They'll be more cooperative, more insightful, and more able to do the work of self-healing.

Well Done!

When the devil came back to see that his man has done his work, he said, "Well done," and went away again.

The Conscious Mind has the power to block the healing process. The primary reason for teaching the client how to perform the tasks is to make sure it's not going to try to run the show. Before taking the lid off the pots, you must teach the client how to set aside thinking, analyzing, and trying to figure anything out.

The client must be willing to let whatever is in the pots be revealed through the process. What's inside the pots? The truth. At least, as the Subconscious Mind has it. Every situation, circumstance, and event that has been condemned, and banished from consciousness, is still there, making the Mind a living hell. And festering inside the cauldrons are pictures, memories, feelings, and emotions that have been too painful to face.

Every person who ever hurt the client in any way, whether in word or deed, is stewing away inside the pots. As a result, they continue to hurt the client *in their Mind*. Taking the lid off those memories will reveal who is responsible for those uncomfortable feelings. But the devil knows better than to force the feeling Mind.

The lids are on those memories for a very good reason. At one time, the feelings associated with those events – fear, anger, hatred, condemnation, sadness, loneliness, guilt, etc. – threatened to overwhelm the client. So, the Subconscious Mind stepped in to protect. That's it's job.

It isn't about to cooperate with you until it's convinced that both you and the client can handle the truth. This reminds me of the movie *A Few Good Men*. Picture Jack Nicholson as the Subconscious Mind and Tom Cruise as the Conscious Mind.

SCM (Jack Nicholson): *You want answers?* CM (Tom Cruise): *I think I'm entitled to them*

SCM: *You want answers?*

CM: *I want the truth!*

SCM: *YOU CAN'T HANDLE THE TRUTH! Son, we live in a world that has walls. And those walls have to be guarded by men with guns. Who's gonna do it? You?*

I have a greater responsibility than you can possibly fathom . . . You have the luxury of not knowing what I know . . . And my existence, while grotesque and incomprehensible to you, saves lives.

YOU DON'T WANT THE TRUTH. Because deep down, in places you don't talk about at parties, you want me on that wall. You need me on that wall.

The devil knows to let the truth be revealed through the process. Releasing work will take off some of the pressure. The more relief the client realizes, the more the Subconscious Mind learns that the client really *can* handle the truth! As this happens, the Subconscious Mind will begin to look for opportunities to get more relief.

The devil also knows to make the client responsible for the results. All healing is self-healing. So, instead of looking into something that could potentially be overwhelming, the devil teaches the client to stay focus on the feeling. The devil employs statements of validation to bring the client's attention to signs of success. Well done! And as the client learns to take ownership of these increments of success, resistance to going there is replaced by curiosity.

Summary

The purpose of the set-up phase is to prepare the client to face the truth as their Subconscious Mind has it. Just as all hypnosis is self-hypnosis, all healing is self-healing. The first objective is to prepare the client for the healing journey.

The Set-Up Phase is comprised of the first three steps in the seven-phase protocol:

1. The Intake Process
2. The Educational Pre-Talk
3. The First Hypnosis Session

The intake allows you to establish a therapeutic relationship and identify the key information needed to guide the healing process effectively. The educational pre-talk allows you to establish a Contract that gives permission for hypnosis to happen and for regression to happen. The first hypnosis session allows you to guide the client into the state required for real regression.

Hypnosis is the optimum state for learning. While in hypnosis, you can teach the client how to do the work required to get a lasting result. This can make it much easier to find and resolve to the causal event. Remember, the client is responsible for the results. After all, it's their Mind! To be successful, he must be ready, willing, and able to do the work necessary to achieve his Therapeutic Goal.

Teaching your client how to find a feeling will help you to access to a bridge to the past. Teaching the client how to release a feeling will give you a client who can face and feel uncomfortable emotions trapped in past events. Validating small wins can pave the way for larger wins as doubt and fear are replaced with hopefulness and enthusiasm for resolving what's been getting in the client's way.

Learn more in the Ready for Regression First Session System Course here: www.tribeofhealers.com/ready-for-regression-first-session-system-course

PHASE 2: TRANSFORM

Transforming Phase	
4 REGRESS TO CAUSE (R2C)	5 INNER CHILD WORK
Locate the Cause	*Re-Story*
4.1 Find a Bridge	5.1 Dialogue Work
4.2 Test for ISE	5.2 Re-Parent Child
4.3 Uncover the Story	5.3 Re-Story the ISE

Hypnotherapy is not like surgery or medicine. It's not just techniques that can be taught. To be a good Hypnotherapist, a person has to have an instinct for it – and inherent kindness and an ancient wisdom. – **Gil Boyne, Transforming Therapy**

CHAPTER 10:
Age Regression (R2C)

T his time the soldier took a good look around, and in every corner of hell the caldrons are boiling and bubbling, with furious fires under them. He'd have loved to look into them, but the devil has expressly forbidden it.

The client may have partial awareness of the cause of the problem. They may recognize some of the contributing factors. But when they cannot figure a way out of the problem, it's because the information needed to solve the problem is not accessible to the Conscious Mind. That information is buried at a Subconscious level of Mind. So, that's where we must go to find the answers.

The problem is that the Conscious Mind wants to try to figure things out. And Conscious mental activity only gets in the way. This is why thinking, analyzing, and trying to figure things out is expressly forbidden by the Contract. Don't look in the pots. *Don't think.* Just follow instructions, focus on the feeling, and respond with your first impression. The client must demonstrate this ability before they're ready to begin Regression to Cause hypnotherapy.

Hypnosis gives us access to the Part of the Mind that is responsible for emotional memories. While a light state of hypnosis naturally enhances a person's ability to recall memories, it's not enough depth to get a real regression. Real regression requires somnambulism. So, you must test for state.

You need somnambulism to revivify an event. Regression is not merely thinking about or remembering a past event. It is a reliving of the experience – seeing, hearing, sensing, and feeling – just as it was the first time. The client steps into the event, and it's all happening now. This allows the underlying cause of the client's symptoms to be brought to conscious awareness.

The principal methods used to locate and resolve the underlying cause of the client's presenting issue include:

1. Bridging Techniques
2. Uncovering Procedures
3. Releasing the Hidden Cause(s)

Bridging Techniques provide a path to the events that are responsible for generating symptoms. The Uncovering Procedure enhances revivification before bringing to light the aspects contributing to the client's issue. Releasing the contributing aspects allows you to resolve the underlying cause(s).

The Two Rs in R2CH

The two Rs in R2CH are regress and release. *Regression* gives access to information trapped in the causal event. *Releasing* removes the Subconscious requirement for symptoms. The secret to achieving a lasting result lies in the releasing. Insight is seldom enough to resolve an emotional issue for good. You need to clear the thoughts and feelings that got trapped in the causal event. This creates the conditions where healing can happen. Hippocrates taught this. Release the blocks, and healing will happen because it's in our nature.

There's a Zen teaching which counsels, "Before enlightenment, chop wood, carry water." This is the devil's counsel. Feed the fires, clean the house. Keep the focus on the feeling. Feeling a feeling releases the feeling. Releasing everything, unlike love, restores the Mind to its natural state of balance and harmony. As a result, unwanted physical symptoms, habits of thought, feelings, reactivity, or behaviors fall away. Love heals.

Human beings are like trees. - Cal Banyan

A Different Mind Model

According to Science, at the core of everything, there is an energy that defines it. Religion calls this energy Spirit, Soul, or the Indwelling God. Psychologically, this is our innate state of simply being "enough." It is here that our Core Programming for happiness, physically, mentally, and emotionally resides.

The Subconscious Mind grows and develops in much the same way a tree does. It grows from the inside out, but this isn't linear; it's a cyclical growth pattern. This is how nature works — everything moves in a spiral. The Conscious Mind is like the bark of the tree. It's the outermost part of the tree as well as the most mature level of Mind. This part of the Mind is responsible for making sense of our environment. Reason and logic help to support decisions in order to meet important needs.

Behind the Conscious Mind are all the rings of growth and development. Each ring represents a year in the life of the tree. And stored in these rings are memories of experiences that made an impression. For example, if the tree survived a drought, bug infestation, or lightning strike, the memory of that experience is still there, recorded in the rings of the tree. Similarly, the Subconscious Mind holds onto all our emotional memories.

Just as an Adult tree grows around the sapling, the Adult Mind grows around the Mind of the Child. Given the right conditions, it will grow and mature into a strong, healthy Adult tree. Just as the sapling is the Part of the tree that holds the genetic code for the whole tree, the very center of Mind holds Nature's blueprint for health and well-being. This is what Hippocrates called *the healing power of nature*. It is still there within each of us. But when we lose conscious awareness of this Deepest Part of us, it becomes Un-Conscious.

The Mind of a Child is wide open and highly suggestible. As a child grows from infancy to adulthood, rings of growth and development form around this Core Self. This forms what we call the Sub-conscious Mind. Held within the Subconscious Mind are the memories of situations which, in the past, made an emotional impression on us. Each memory is stored, for future reference, within the ring that represents the age at which the experience occurred. If the cause of a problem occurred in an event at two years of age, that event is still alive, held within the second ring of the tree. The Child in that event is the Conscious Mind *at that time*.

The Subconscious Mind is the Conscious Mind *of the past*. What this means is that when you regress a client into an event in childhood, you are speaking to the Conscious Mind of the client *at that age*. As you regress to earlier and earlier events, you're moving closer to the center of the tree where the blueprint, or genetic code, or ancestral memory for a healthy state of consciousness resides.

This is the Core information with which the tree started out. A state of simply Being. A state of Enough-ness, independent of external conditions. Healing is a process of reconnecting a person with the awareness of this energetic Source.

The ISE

Regression theory states that, in the absence of an organic cause, the source of the problem is to be found in the client's history. Symptoms don't just come out of nowhere. Something had to happen to cause them.

Every problem is the result of life experience. Regression to Cause is a process of locating the event that caused the problem. This event is called the Initial Sensitizing Event (ISE). The ISE is the experience that caused the client to become sensitive to something in particular. Any event that is related to the client's issue but comes *after* the ISE is called a Subsequent Sensitizing Event (SSE).

SSEs

An SSE is like fertilizer to the ISE. It feeds the problem by acting as a reminder of the ISE. Every time the client bumps into a situation that reminds them of the ISE, either consciously or unconsciously, it reinforces the underlying, unresolved problem.

Once a person has been sensitized, repeated stimulation of the pattern will have a compounding effect. This is what Subsequent Sensitizing Events do. They're not the *cause* of the problem. They're reinforcing it, making it stronger. Every time the pattern gets re-stimulated, the symptoms get a little worse. This is why problems tend to get worse over time.

Remember the stack of bricks? If you look at the pyramid-shaped pile of bricks in reflection, you'll see an inverted pyramid. This illustrates how events stack up over time. The first brick is the causal event. It's the ISE. Each subsequent brick is a Subsequent Sensitizing Event (SSE), which strengthens the underlying pattern by validating the perceptions, thoughts, and feelings established in the casual event. With each validation, the pattern is reinforced, making it stronger.

Eventually, the whole thing gains enough momentum to produce symptoms. The time this takes really depends on how many repetitions were involved. The more frequency of events, the sooner symptoms will emerge. Other issues can get added to the mix as the pattern continues to grow and develop through Subsequent Events. These, however, are *secondary* issues and are usually easy to clear once you have pulled the plug on the ISE.

The SPE

The proverbial "straw that breaks the camel's back" is referred to as the Symptom Producing Event (SPE). That's when symptoms appear. The symptoms might be:

- Irrational or obsessive thoughts, e.g., self-criticism

- Overwhelming feelings, e.g., phobia, anxiety, rage

- Unwanted behaviors. e.g., overeating, smoking, excessive hand-washing

- Physical complaints, e.g., hives, diabetes, cancer

What these issues all have in common is that they're *symptoms* of an underlying problem trapped inside the Initial Sensitizing Event. The Initial Sensitizing Event (ISE) is the first time the client ever experienced a particular pattern of perceptions, thoughts, and feelings. This is what's responsible for the client's thoughts, feelings, and behaviors now. The goal is to find a Bridge to the ISE.

Love brings up everything unlike itself to be healed. — **Sondra Ray**

CHAPTER 11:
Find a Bridge to the Past

This time the soldier took a good look around, and in every corner of hell, the caldrons are boiling and bubbling, with furious fires under them. He'd have loved to look into them, but the devil has expressly forbidden it.

The Subconscious Mind is the Child Mind. So, what happens when you tell a child, "Don't look!?" They can't help themselves. They can't *not look!* Adam and Eve were instructed not to eat the fruit of the Tree of Knowledge of Good and Evil. But Eve was curious.

The name Eve means *living or life*. It is in our nature to be curious. Curiosity motivates us to seek out what we need in life. It helps to keep us alive by satisfying important needs for things like food, shelter, a mate, safety, and security.

Pandora was curious. She was told not to look, but she took the lid off, anyway. In so doing, she released all the Spites. The Spites are all the feelings trapped inside. Keeping the lid on feelings is called repression. Or suppression. Or depression. Repression is like holding a ball below the surface of the water. It creates internal pressure. The bigger the ball, the more pressure is required to keep it submerged, and the more energy invested in keeping it there.

Eventually, the Subconscious pressure will become too much. When that happens, the *ball* of emotional energy will just pop up into consciousness, bringing with it once forbidden knowledge hidden in the past event. This is essentially what happens when a person gets triggered. They regress. The devil knows this. The devil also knows that you can't think your way back to the ISE. So, don't look. Let it be revealed through the process.

Find a Bridge

At last, he could no longer restrain himself. The temptation became too much, and he lifted the lid off the first caldron, just a little, and peeked inside. And what did he discover but his old sergeant. "Aha, you dog!" he said, "You here? You made it hot for me! Now I'll make it hot for you."

The devil knows that all things are connected because they share the same Source. As a result, the Mind can easily associate back into a past experience. This is because there's a connection between the problem now and the event that caused it. That connection is a Bridge to the Past.

A Bridge is an energetic pathway that exists between two or more events. What connects these events is something they share in common. It might be a thought. It might be an emotion. It might be a physical sensation. Because the Bridge already exists, all you have to do is find it, and you can follow it back to its inception. That's the ISE.

If the shared connection between events is a thought, it's called a Cognitive Bridge. If the connection is a sensation in the body, it's called a Somatic Bridge. If the connection is emotional, it's called an Affect Bridge.

Affect Bridge

Affect Bridge is a hypnoanalytic term coined by John Watkins in 1961. Watkins recognized the tendency of the Mind to associate. You can remember memory A, which reminds you of memory B, which leads you to memory C, and so on. In hypnosis, we rely primarily on Affect Bridge because the link between Memory A and all the other memories is an energetic connection.

Memory A is the ISE. What's holding that memory in place is a specific energy. It's an identifiable feeling. Focusing attention on *that feeling* will give you the most direct Bridge to the causal event. For example, at the symptom level, the problem might be expressing as a craving or a compulsion but behind that feeling is an emotion like fear or anger. Emotions drive behavior. They're there to motivate us to take action. The question is – What caused the emotion or activated that feeling?

You can use a Cognitive Bridge, a Somatic Bridge, or Affect Bridge to regress to the ISE, but the preferred method for regression hypnotherapy is Affect Bridge. This is because the one thing that every SSE has in common with the ISE is an emotion.

Every event will contain thoughts and feelings and sensations, but these things are all linked together *emotionally*. Emotion is the native language of the Subconscious Mind. This emotional energy signature makes Affect Bridge the most direct path to the causal event.

Cognitive Bridge

A Cognitive Bridge is the process of following a thought. Freud's approach was to follow a chain of thoughts or free association. If you can identify a recurring or obsessive thought, you can use it to Bridge back to the first time the client ever thought that thought.

Clients who have a lot of negative self-talk are playing old tapes over and over again. They're stuck in a loop. The problem with this constant replaying of a thought is that it's constantly reinforcing the uncomfortable feelings. It's making things worse.

Because the thought and feeling are connected, focusing attention on the thought, it will automatically bring up the emotion connected to it. As a result, you can convert a Cognitive Bridge into an Affect Bridge. When the client thinks *that thought,* how does it make them feel? Where do they feel that feeling in the body? What emotion might that be? This can give you a more direct route to the ISE.

Somatic Bridge

A Somatic Bridge is where you use a physical sensation such as tension, pressure, or pain in the body to Bridge back to the cause. The lump, or bump, or ache, or pain that the client is experiencing, is a signal from the past that can be followed back to its source. For example, in a session with Stephen Parkhill, I was focusing on a breast lump.

An uncomfortable sensation in the body is often associated with an unresolved emotion. In my case, the lump converted to an emotion that took me right back into the womb. You can't consciously remember an experience in the womb! And that's where the root of the problem was.

The Watch & Wait Method

Whoever said 'time heals all wounds' was dead wrong. Conscious memories of painful childhood events may fade over time, but at a Subconscious level, they are still alive and well. As such, they still have the power to hurt the client, even decades later.

That feeling which are keeping the caldrons bubbling and boiling could be fear, anger, sadness, or something else, but it's connected to every time the client ever felt that way. Sooner or later, the Subconscious Mind is going to associate back into a past situation that has everything to do with that feeling. That's when the lid will come off the pot, and the client will step into a past event. You just have to wait for it to happen.

I learned something about standing back and letting things happen from watching a Master of Aikido. The teacher, a short Japanese man, wished to demonstrate to a group of nine-year-old boys how to work with their staves. After eliciting the help of a volunteer, he then instructed the boy to stand six feet away, at the end of the mat, and ready himself to launch an attack.

The boy's task was to run at his teacher and, with all his might, try to strike the little man with the stave. The boy was clearly enthused with the assigned task, launching his attack vigorously and running full-tilt toward the teacher. The teacher, on the other hand, appeared unmoved by a rapidly approaching attacker. He stood his ground until the very last moment.

Just as the boy was about to strike his target, the little man deftly stepped aside. He didn't resist or oppose his assailant in any way. He simply and elegantly turned his body 90 degrees and took one step back. The boy, now fully committed to his path, was unable to stop his forward momentum. He looked very surprised as he stumbled awkwardly past his target.

A whisper of a grin passed across the little man's face as the boy stumbled, head first, onto the mat. And, adding insult to injury, as the boy went down, the teacher raised his staff and gently tapped the bewildered lad on his butt.

Similar to the student, your client must be willing to participate in the process. As the teacher, your job is to encourage the client to stay focused on the feeling and hold nothing back. As the feeling gets stronger, it will start to take over. The intensity will pick up momentum. When this happens, you can give the Subconscious Mind a gentle tap in the right direction by giving the suggestion to follow the feeling back to an earlier event. Then, step aside and let nature its course.

The Most Powerful Bridge

Affect Bridge gives you the most direct path to the root of the problem, making it the backbone of regression to cause hypnotherapy. This is why the devil teaches the client how to work with feelings and emotions first.

But if you can connect a thought, *and* a feeling, *and* a sensation in the body, and have the client focus on all three at once, this will give you a powerful bridge to the past. For example, let's say the thought is, *I'm not good enough*. That thought is going to generate an emotion such as fear. Emotions are experienced in the body. Let's say that this particular fear is being experienced in the body as a knot in the gut. You now have a *powerful* bridge to the past.

The more specific you can be, the better your results will be. If you can target a specific thought-feeling-sensation pattern, it will give you a very specific Bridge to follow. The thought, *I'm not good enough, which makes me feel scared in my gut,* gives you a very specific signal to follow back to its roots.

#1. Find the Feeling

"Aha, you dog!" he said, "You here? You made it hot for me! Now I'll make it hot for you."

The easiest way to find a feeling for regression is to start with a recent triggering event. Just talking about this experience will provoke the feeling to come out of its hidey-hole. When that happens, bring the client's attention to that feeling. Find *the feeling* in the body. Then, guide the client to name the emotion.

Remember, emotions are targeted in the torso - primarily in the throat, the chest, and the gut. The instant the client names the emotion, validate it by saying, "There's the feeling!" Then, quantify the feeling.

How strong is that feeling?

#2. Quantify the Feeling

You need a strong Bridge to follow back to the causal event. To quantify a feeling, ask the client to rate the intensity on a scale of 1 to 10. This is called a Subjective Unit of Discomfort/Distress (SUD). To take a SUD, ask the client to focus on the feeling in their body. Then ask, "On a scale of 1 – 10, where ten is the strongest it's ever been, how strong is that feeling (in your gut) right now?"

If it's a seven or higher, you have enough intensity for a Bridge. If it's less than a ten, get the client's permission to turn up the volume on that feeling. Stir up the fire. Tell them, "That feeling has everything to do with the reason you're here. We need that feeling to be at least a ten. Would you be willing to let it come up to a ten so we can take care of it?" With the client's permission, you can proceed to amplify the feeling.

#3. Stir up the Feeling

Whereupon, he dropped the lid, stirred up the fire, and put on some more wood.

Affect Bridge is a very natural process. It's also pretty easy to facilitate. Just have the client focus on the feeling, test to make sure you have a strong Bridge, then instruct the client to follow that feeling back to an earlier time they felt that feeling. The trick is to stir up the feeling powerfully because you need a strong Bridge that will carry you all the way back to the ISE. If you brought up a feeling of fear, have the client focus on the emotion of fear. Make sure they're really feeling it! Where in the body do they feel that fear? In the throat? The gut? The chest?

Keep the focus on that as you proceed to amplify the feeling. The traditional approach to amplifying a feeling is just a direct suggestion count-up. For example, "In a moment, I'm going to count from 1 to 10. As I do, let that feeling come up powerfully within you, understanding that . . . that feeling is allowed to be there. And your permission to allow that feeling . . . to be felt and released . . . is what allows you to heal". This tells the client what to do – let the feeling come up to a ten. It then provides a reason for allowing this to happen.

The count-up then proceeds with intermittent suggestions to amplify the intensity or strength of the feeling. For example, "One . . . there's the feeling . . . Two . . . coming up powerfully within you . . . you feel the feeling," and so on.

An alternative approach is to start your count up at whatever the client's SUD level was. For example, if the client says it's a seven, then start your count at seven. "There's the feeling. It's a seven. You can feel it in your chest. Coming up to eight now. You feel the feeling." And just keep counting up until you get to ten. This approach is more congruent with the client's subjective experience, but either way works.

When you get to ten, take another SUD to verify that it's up to ten. Ask the client, "On a scale of 1 to 10 … how strong is that feeling?" If it's at least a ten, you know that the client is following instructions and has stirred up the fires enough to provide a Bridge back to the ISE.

Stir Up the Feeling Patter

Focus on that feeling. As you focus on it, it continues to grow. That feeling is allowed to be here. And your permission to allow that feeling to be felt and released is what allows you to heal. Understand?

As you focus on that feeling, it continues to grow. As I count from 1 to 5 (or 7 to 10), that feeling bubbles up to the surface. It grows as strong and as real as you've ever known it before. Let that happen. This is the perfect place for it.

ONE – There's the feeling. It's that feeling inside that you just don't like. You can feel it in your body. It doesn't feel good.

TWO – Coming up powerfully within you, now, bubbling up to the surface, you feel the feeling. And on the next count, there's the feeling, as strong as you've ever known it before.

THREE – Growing stronger, now, welling up to the surface, you feel the feeling.

FOUR – More powerfully, now. You feel the feeling! And on the next count, like the floodgates of a dam burst open, there's the feeling.

FIVE! – There's the feeling! That feeling is a signal to the past. It's connected to every event you ever felt that feeling, all the way back to the beginning.

#4. Follow the Feeling

Next, he went to the second caldron, lifted the lid a little, and looked in. This one had his lieutenant inside. "Aha, you dog!" he said, "You here? You made it hot for me! Now I'll make it hot for you." He closed the lid again and fetched yet another log to make it really hot.

Because the Subconscious Mind works through association, it will show you the events that have everything to do with that feeling. But the Subconscious Mind will seldom go directly to the ISE. Sometimes, that is just a bridge too far, especially when the ISE is located in early childhood. So, when Bridging back, instruct the client to go back to an *earlier* time that they felt that feeling (fear, anger, sadness, etc.).

Remember, the ISE is merely the first time the client ever felt *that feeling*. Subsequent events then add to the unresolved pattern, increasing internal pressure. This is why we want to do the bulk of the work in the ISE. It's the event with the least emotional charge associated with it, making it much easier to face and feel.

SSEs represent more pressing issues because there's more pressure in an SSE than at the ISE. As a result, you're more likely to land in a Subsequent Sensitizing Event simply because the emotional charge in that event is stronger.

If there are multiple emotions contributing to the problem, choose the one with the most intensity to Bridge back on. Remember, you need a strong Bridge to go the distance to the ISE. Take a SUD and focus on the one with the biggest charge to it. Emotional intensity is like rocket fuel for a launch!

The chain of events responsible for generating the symptoms is connected by the same feeling. That's the Bridge. The secret to Bridging back is to make sure that you are following an actual emotion such as fear, anger, or sadness, then stick with that emotion. If you try to Bridge back on anxiety or depression, you will get nowhere. You need a real emotion.

By keeping the focus on a specific emotion — the fear, the sadness, the anger — you can hop from lily pad to lily pad, all the way back to the ISE. Just don't change horse in mid-stream. If you are tracking back on sadness, stay with the sadness. If you're following anger, stay with the anger.

Other emotions will be revealed as you regress into earlier and earlier events. Make a note of them but stay with the primary emotion you chose to Bridge back on. That's the feeling you are following back to its root. Subsequent events contribute additional aspects to the overall pattern. This makes it easy to get sidetracked. For example, if you're following anger, and it changes to fear, keep the focus on the anger. Once you have committed to a specific Bridge, keep the focus *on that feeling* until you reach the end of the line.

Affect Bridge Patter

There's the feeling! I'm going to count from 5 down to 1. On the count of 1, your mind has you back in an earlier scene, situation, or event that has everything to do with that feeling.

FIVE – Going back in time.

FOUR – To a scene, situation, or event of significance to that feeling.

THREE – Arms and legs may be growing smaller now as your mind takes you further and further back.

TWO – Moving right into that event of significance. The scene grows vivid, real, and clear. And on the next count, there you are, as real as the first time.

And ONE – There you are. Say, Here I am. . . [wait for the client to repeat] . . . And I feel [put an ending on it] . . . [wait for the client to repeat].

Once you have verified that (a) the client is present at the event and (b) the client is still feeling the feeling, you can proceed to uncover the Story about what happened in that event.

Release Resistance

If you're following anger and it turns to fear, don't get sidetracked. Don't start following the fear. The fear is actually resistance. The way to deal with resistance is to release it. If you don't, the lid will drop back down, and you'll lose the Bridge to the ISE. But if you release the fear, you'll discover the anger is right there, beneath it. Validate the anger. Give it permission to be there. Then, Bridge back off of it.

Most of us have been taught that anger is bad. So, the first step in dealing with anger may entail learning not to be afraid of it. Anger is a natural human emotion. Anger is there for a reason. It's meant to empower the person in the face of a threat. And when we've been hurt, we feel angry. That's good! Anger is there to motivate us to *do something* so we can feel better. The problem with *this* anger is that it's stuck inside, hurting the client and everyone who loves him. So, give the anger permission to be there.

Recognize that this event is something the Subconscious has been stewing over for years, breeding dis-ease. Admitting, *I feel angry!* can be something of a revelation for a client who has been taught to keep a lid on his bad feelings. They begin to recognize that they cannot help feeling angry about what was done to them. Validating statements like, "I feel angry! I feel it in my body! I'm allowed to feel this feeling! This is my feeling!" will help to bring authentic feelings of anger to the surface and fuel the client's enthusiasm to get it out.

To release the anger, start with the more general and move to the more specific. Begin by releasing all the thoughts and feelings associated with the event itself (i.e., what happened). Then, release the specific thoughts and feelings toward the individual players (i.e., the Offender and anyone else who's there). Often, the Offender was a loved-one — parent, grandparent, caregiver, sibling, etc. Getting it out can only change things for the better. So, stoke up the fire! Then, encourage the client to express how they feel. The more the client focuses on the feelings and sensations associated with the person who hurt them, the more energy will be available for release.

"One huge thing that stood out to me, which they all experienced in the service, was a horrific sense of betrayal. They all felt betrayed by a superior officer, by their branch of the service, by their country, or by someone or something. This got layered onto whatever other betrayals they had already experienced in life. The anger that they held onto often kept a trauma alive. They wanted to keep that anger and that sense

of betrayal in order to keep alive thoughts about punishing whoever or whatever they were mad at. That's like drinking poison and hoping the person you're mad at gets sick and dies." — **EFT for PTSD**

Keeping a lid on anger takes up a lot of energy. That energy can be utilized for healing! When anger surfaces, bringing the intensity level down will give the client immediate relief. Begin by having the client rate the level of anger they're feeling in the body with a Subjective Unit of Distress Scale (SUDS).

Tapping will release low-level anger, but having a pillow available to the client for punching is ideally suited for purging an abscessed wound. The bigger the anger, the bigger the movement called for. Match the power of the movement to the strength of the feeling. Annoyed or irritated is lower on the intensity meter than mad, angry, or enraged. However, the degree of anger that's being experienced by the client is not always apparent. I have had clients who appear quite calm, who then report feeling rage.

Facing up to old authority figures and giving them hell feels good! Give the client a really big pillow to go to work on and watch for the grin as they pump, release, and express their anger into the pillow for the first time. Let them discover it's okay to feel this most *forbidden* of feelings. They will not be struck by lightning, and nobody will die if they release their anger in a healthy way.

As the client releases the feelings toward the Offender, they are allowed to speak directly to the Offender and find the words that go with the feeling. Whatever needs to be said, they're allowed to say it. The only rule is to let it *all* out. Saying out loud, "You hurt me! You made my life so miserable! I hate you!" is not being negative. It's finally admitting the truth of how you feel. And you know what they say, "The truth shall set you free."

Saying, "You hurt me! You made me feel," does not make the client bad. It offers validation, relief, and empowerment and reminds the client that all their feelings are good. Even the angry ones. Saying, "I don't have to carry this for the rest of my life," reminds the client that there is a good reason for releasing the feeling. All the pain they have endured because of this event/person can finally be let go.

Realize that what was missing the first time was the *expression* of these *bad* thoughts, *bad* words, and *bad feelings*. Getting it out puts an end to the pain. The client needs to know this. They also need to know that feelings are finite. Even anger, resentment, rage, condemnation, and hate won't last very long when allowed, felt, and expressed. Releasing them creates space for good feelings to flow back into the client. As a result, the client will experience a new level of peace and clarity, which can open the door to deeper healing.

Releasing anger is an act of empowerment that will burn away unnecessary fear and resistance, making it easier for you to find the ISE. Don't worry about losing the Bridge. That signal is coming out of the event that caused it. It hasn't gone anywhere. And once the fear that was blocking its expression is out of the way, the client will be able to face the truth about how much pain those past experiences caused them.

The Woodchopper

Here's a useful yoga movement that is specifically designed for releasing anger. The *woodchopper* takes a stance with feet planted firmly on the ground, knees slightly bent, and heels about two feet apart. He raises his arms together over the head with hands joined and arches his back slightly. Then, making an "ah" sound on the descent, he swings the whole upper portion of the body downward, bringing his hands between his legs and through, as if swinging an ax.

The motion should be smooth and rapid, emitting as much force and power as is possible while letting the sound be full and loud, "Hah!" As an exercise, it can be repeated five to ten times in a session. The feeling of energy will break through into the upper body as it fulfills its purpose of releasing the anger.

You can improvise the woodchopper to session-based work. For example, you could use it as a warm-up to Pillow Work or as a homework exercise for releasing residual anger. Find creative ways to encourage your clients to get it out!

Spontaneous Regression

The most common approach to Affect Bridge is to provoke a feeling and follow it back into earlier events. The devil, however, works with Nature. He knows that, sooner or later, regression will happen. You just have to watch and wait for it. Often, changes in the body will indicate that the client is stepping into a past event. You have to watch carefully because the client may be so preoccupied with where their Mind is taking them that they won't tell you what's happening. Watch the body. The body never lies.

You might notice the eyes moving back and forth behind the eyelids, indicating visual activity. This may be accompanied by a subtle shift in vocal tonality. For example, the client might start speaking more quietly or in a more childlike tone. You might observe a physical reaction such as blushing, twitching, or quivering. A tear might roll down the cheek.

The client may say something like, "I'm remembering when my dog died." This tells you the Subconscious Mind has taken the client to that event. Something is being brought to conscious awareness. As the event is bubbling up to the surface of consciousness, the client is regressing into the feeling. When this happens, you may be tempted to explore what's happening, but it's too soon for that. You need to make sure you have a strong enough Bridge to get to the ISE. Keep the focus on the feeling.

Some clients will spontaneously regress into a painful event. When this happens, they may abreact. This tells you that their Subconscious Mind trusts you enough to show you where the pain is coming from. It's telling you that it wants some relief. This is great news! But it can come as a big surprise to suddenly be dumped into a scene from childhood that doesn't feel very good!

While the Subconscious Mind may be ready to face what's there, it doesn't mean the Conscious Mind is prepared for it. You need to encourage the client to allow the feeling to be there by providing safety, keeping the focus on the feeling, and working quickly.

#1. Provide Safety

Job #1 is safety. When the Subconscious Mind takes the client into a painful past event, realize that what the Conscious Mind wants is a sense of control. The problem is that the Conscious Mind can't control an emotion. It doesn't have the power. *You do.* Reassure the client that *they've got this.* Let the client know that everything is under control. It's all happening exactly the way it should, and you know exactly what to do.

Remind the client that, "That feeling has everything to do with the reason you're here! If you can feel it, you can heal it! The only place it can hurt you is trapped inside!"

#2. Focus on the Feeling

The Conscious Mind has the power to block the feeling. You need the client to follow your instructions so you can take care of it. Give good reasons for allowing the feeling to bubble up to the surface powerfully. Then, immediately give the command, *Stay focused on that feeling.* Tend the fire by keeping the focus of attention on the feeling in the body.

That feeling is Subconscious Mind's way of communicating, and it's saying, *Hey! There's a problem here!* It's by following the feeling, whether consciously or unconsciously, that the client has spontaneously stepped into a scene, a situation, or an event that has everything to do with that feeling. Keep the Conscious Mind focused on the feeling. That's what's calling for healing.

Tell the client, "Your Subconscious Mind has just shown us what's calling for healing. Let yourself stay focused on that feeling". Then, move straight into the uncovering procedure and find out what's happening in that situation to cause that feeling.

#3. Work Quickly!

As you proceed with the uncovering procedure, work quickly. You need to stay ahead of the client's learned coping strategies. Don't give the client time to think. Remember, thinking just gets in the way.

Remind the client, *Don't think! Feel the answer.* Then, move right into the uncovering procedure. You need to work quickly to stay ahead of the

Conscious Mind. The Conscious Mind has been taught to avoid uncomfortable feelings, especially when they don't make sense.

When a feeling just comes out of nowhere, it's irrational. You need to provide a reason for the client to stay present in the event long enough to find out what that's happening. For example, "Your Subconscious Mind knows why you're here. It brought us here for a reason, so you can heal. Let yourself stay focused on the feeling! First impression."

Remember, the feeling is always there for a reason. Something happened to cause it. You need to find out what's happening in the event to cause the feeling. This is the purpose of the uncovering procedure.

Summary

All events are connected by a thread. The thread may be a thought, a physical sensation, or an emotion. While you can use any of these things to Bridge back on, Affect Bridge gives you a very organic approach to guiding a client back to the root cause of the problem. This is because what's holding the memory in place is the feeling. And it's the *emotional charge* trapped in the event that keeps the problem active.

Whatever that feeling might be – - fear, anger, sadness, or whatever – something happened to cause it. But to identify the event that caused that feeling in the first place, you need a strong Bridge. The stronger the feeling, the stronger the Bridge is to the past. This is the secret to Bridging back – make sure you have a strong Bridge.

The way to access a strong Bridge is to hone in on it. You need the Conscious Mind to be focused on one *thing*. Keep the focus on just one thought, or one feeling, or one specific sensation in the body. Remember, that thought or feeling or sensation is a signal that is coming out of the event that caused it. It acts like GPS. All you need to do is keep the Conscious Mind focused on *that*, and it's like targeting the ISE.

Once you have a strong Bridge, all you have to do is instruct the client to go back to an earlier time they had that thought or felt that feeling. Trust the Subconscious Mind to guide you.

The steps to the Bridging Process are:

1. Find the feeling in the body
2. Quantify the feeling
3. Stir up the feeling
4. Follow the Feeling

CHAPTER 12:
Locate the ISE

Then, he wanted to see who might be shut up in the third kettle. It was actually a general! "Aha, you dog!" he said, "You here? You made it hot for me! Now I'll make it hot for you." And he fetched the bellows and made hell-fire flare well up under him.

The process of Bridging back will reveal a series of SSEs. The goal is to locate the ISE so that you can identify all the factors that are contributing to the client's problem. Once you know what's causing the problem, you can release it. Clear everything, and there's nothing left to cause a problem. This is how you get a lasting result.

Regression does not reveal facts about what happened. It reveals how the Subconscious Mind recorded the event. Regression allows you to uncover the Story about how that specific experience was perceived and was responded to mentally, emotionally, and physiologically *at that time*. That's it.

When a person is in a stress-response, aspects of what's happening can get distorted or be completely overlooked. This is because the thinking goes offline when we're facing a perceived threat to survival. When that happens, the experience doesn't get recorded accurately. If the situation was too overwhelming, repression most likely occurred.

Repression is a healthy, self-protective mechanism that is necessary for survival early in life. The problem is that it contributes to problems later in life. Even if the client regresses into a consciously-remembered event, there will be aspects of that experience that have not been accessible to conscious awareness. This will bring up resistance.

Resistance

The uncovering procedure makes the unconscious conscious. As a result, there's always going to be some resistance to allowing the details to come to full awareness. The Conscious Mind will naturally want to question the process. Don't let that happen. Keep the focus on the feeling. The feeling is the key that opens the door to the event. When you count back into the event, don't give the client any time to think. For example, "5, 4, 3, 2, 1 – BE THERE!"

Be there is the first suggestion. You want the client to step into the event. To verify that the client is stepping into the event, use autosuggestion. Instruct the client to say, "Here I am," waiting for the client to repeat. This instructs the client to step fully into the event. Then, add, "And I feel [put an ending on it]" waiting for the client to repeat. This allows you to verify that the client is still connected to their feelings.

If the client hesitates, verify that the feeling is still there, "True or false, you feel the feeling?"

If the client has lost the feeling, you need to find it again. It's that simple. Start over. Provoke the feeling, quantify the feeling, amplify the feeling, Bridge back. Work quickly. Don't give the client time to think. "5, 4, 3, 2, 1 – BE THERE! The first impression is?"

Never proceed to the next step until the client has successfully completed the step that you're on. Make the client responsible for the results. If the client says, "I don't know," or "Nothing," they are not stepping into the event. Back up a step and find the feeling, again. Always keep the focus on the feeling. That's how the Subconscious Mind communicates.

Preliminary Uncovering

When the client has successfully completed the initial steps into the event, what follows are the initial three uncovering questions.

Stay focused on that (scared) feeling in your (gut) . . .

1. *First impression, does it feel like it's* daytime or night time?
2. *First impression, does it feel like you're* inside or outside?
3. *First impression, does it feel like you're* alone or with someone?

The purpose of these first three questions is to encourage revivification. The client is not remembering the event. They are stepping into the event and reviewing it through the eyes of their younger self. This gives you access to the hidden details trapped in the event.

Notice how these questions begin with the most general perspective and gradually narrow the focus down to more specific details about the event? They guide the client to associate more fully with the scene. Don't skip this important stage of the uncovering procedure.

The minute the client answers the first question, you're in! You have successfully taken the lid off the pot. This will allow all the details of what's happening in that situation to bubble up into consciousness. The key information you need to uncover is Who, What, When, Where, and How.

1. Who else is there?
2. What is happening?
3. When is this event happening? (At what age?)
4. Where is this scene playing out? (Schoolyard, living room, bedroom, etc.)
5. How does this make the client feel?

The uncovering questions are always delivered using present-tense to encourage a reliving of the event rather than merely remembering. Keep your language clean by relying primarily on multiple-choice questions or open-ended sentences. This ensures that you are not leading the client.

Remember, a person in hypnosis is highly suggestible. Questions like, "Are you with Mom?" or "Do you feel scared?" act as suggestions. "Are you alone or with someone?" or "What feeling are you feeling?" on the other hand, elicit only the client's perceptions. This will allow you to avoid contaminating the results.

Test for the ISE

When you're Bridging back, the goal is to locate the ISE. You don't need to spend a lot of time uncovering all the details in an SSE. Keep your eye on the prize! A little preliminary uncovering will give you a general sense of what's happening in that event. Then, once you have a sense of the Story, conduct a test for the ISE.

The process always follows the same steps.

1. Bridge to an earlier event.
2. Preliminary Uncovering to get a sense of the Story.
3. Test for the ISE.
4. Continue Bridging back until you locate the ISE.

The following four tests will help you to feel confident that you have, indeed, located the causal event.

#1. The Age Test

The problem is *not* what happened in the event. The problem has to do with how what was happening was being interpreted at that time. This has everything to do with the age at which it occurred. The first test for the ISE is the Age Test. How young is the client in the event?

Most of the time, the ISE will occur prior to the formation of the Critical Faculty around age five or six. Before this, the Child lacks the cognitive and emotional maturity with which to make sense of his experience. Situations in childhood can easily be misinterpreted. This is certainly what we find in regression sessions. Most of the time, the cause of the problem turns out to be no big deal.

Not every ISE occurs in childhood. A traumatic event in adult life could qualify as an ISE. For example, an event of violence, a rape, surviving a major car crash could be a seed-planting event. But you still have to test. A traumatic event in adult life could merely be a Symptom Producing Event. Dr. Robert Scaer is a neurologist and psychologist who specializes in trauma. He discovered that patients, who failed to respond to standard treatment for physical injuries, often had an underlying, unresolved trauma in childhood.

These patients continued to suffer from persistent pain and chronic symptoms because they weren't just dealing with a physical injury. There was an underlying emotional problem that was preventing them from healing. Psychologically, they were stuck in a traumatic experience that had sensitized them very early in life. It was this earlier trauma that was screaming for resolution through the symptoms. The event that occurred later in life merely acted as a trigger for the underlying, unresolved pattern.

If your client Bridges back to a traumatic event in adolescence or adult life, don't assume that you have located the ISE. Test. Verify that you have actually found the causal event. Some SSEs can be big, hairy-scary experiences. This is mainly due to the internal pressure that has been accumulating over time. When the Subconscious Mind brings you to a big, hairy-scary event, realize there's a lot of emotional intensity trapped in that event. It's because of the Compounding Effect over time. As a result, the experience of that event was much worse than it needed to be.

Releasing the emotional charge trapped in the ISE first will bring down the overall charge around the issue. This is because you will have removed the source of energy that's been feeding into Subsequent Events. You can then come back to clear the event of adult trauma (and you need to do that), and you'll find that the intensity of the event will be significantly reduced.

But to gain access to the ISE, you need to earn the trust of the Subconscious Mind. The Subconscious Mind's Prime Directive is to protect. If the client lands in a big, hairy-scary event, the first step is always to provide safety. Reassure the client that they've got this. Then, help them to release some of the energy trapped in the event.

You don't have to resolve the whole experience in an SSE. Just relieve some of the pressure so that the client can speak. Then, reassure the client that you're going to take care of this situation *in a moment*. Instruct the client to *put a bookmark* on it so that you can come back to it.

The Subconscious Mind needs to know that you're not going to leave the situation hanging. Let it know that you're not ignoring its call for help. Then, bring the focus back to the feeling. That feeling is coming out of the ISE. Focus on the feeling and give the instruction to go back to the first time they *felt that feeling*. If there's sufficient pressure, you might get lucky and go directly to the ISE. Yay!

Most of the time, though, the Subconscious Mind will take you to an earlier event. Like an insect to light, it's attracted to the events that are emitting the strongest signal. That's not the ISE. The ISE is almost always the weakest link in the chain of events.

This is the primary reason for doing the work in the ISE. The emotional charge in the ISE is much weaker. This means there's less resistance to deal with. It's simply easier – for both you and the client – to deal with the first time than it is to try to process a big ball of accumulated energy in a subsequent event. Plus, you won't run the risk of re-traumatizing the client by requiring them to relive a horrific event in adulthood. That's just not necessary.

Releasing the emotional charge in the ISE will help to restore balance to the Mind-body system. As a result, the client will feel calmer and more relaxed and will be able to think more clearly. This will make everything you do *after* that much easier.

#2. The Feeling Test

The Child doesn't have the ability to regulate feelings and emotions because his brain is still developing. As a result, small things can seem insurmountable to a Child. While the ISE may seem like no big deal to Adult Consciousness, *to the Child,* what's happening can feel overwhelming. This is where the second test for the ISE comes in.

The Feeling Test is where you ask the Child, "Is that feeling new or familiar? Is that scared feeling [in your gut] a new feeling or an old familiar feeling? Is that sad feeling [in your heart] new or familiar?"

If you're at the ISE, the feeling you were bridging back on will be new. This is because the ISE is the first time the client ever experienced *that feeling.* The test is not the question, however. Remember, you're dealing with the perceptions of a Child. If there's something about the event that is new, the Child might just tell you that the feeling is new when, in fact, it is not.

If you're dealing with a very *young* Child, you may not always get accurate information. This is why we need multiple tests. Children lack the ability to interpret things accurately. And young children compartmentalize their feelings. A child can be feeling good one moment and bad the next. They may tell you that the bad feeling is new when it's not. It's just that the Child isn't feeling it in the moment. Regardless of the answer, instruct the client to go back to the *first time* they ever felt that feeling.

If the client tells you that the feeling is an old, familiar feeling, Bridge back further. If they tell you that the feeling is new, Bridge back further. Give the instruction, "Focus on that feeling and go back to the first time you ever felt that feeling. That's the test."

The test is the client's response to your instruction to go back to the first time. If the feeling is really and truly new, the client will come back to the same event. If the client bounces back into an earlier event, now you know - that event was an SSE. In this case, continue to Bridge back and continue testing.

If the client bounces back into the same event, you probably have the ISE. This can be a bit tricky, though, because sometimes the client will come back to the same event, but it will be a few minutes or hours before the scene you landed in the first time. This actually can give you a more accurate beginning to the Story. This gives you the place to begin the Inner Child Work.

The Age Test is based on the formation of the Critical Faculty. But I found that most of the time, the ISE is located before the age of three. When you consider the Feeling Test, this begins to make sense. Every basic emotion – fear, anger, sadness, hurt - has usually been experienced by age two or three. If the client is 12, it's unlikely that you've found the ISE. If they're five, maybe. If they've gone back to the womb – bingo!

#3. The Security Test

If you are at the ISE, the Child won't see what's about to happen because there is nothing in his history to compare it to. As a result, there's no warning system in place. The ISE begins the moment the Child is taken by surprise. If the client passes the Age Test and the Feeling Text, the third test is for Safety and Security.

Instruct the client to go *before* anything bad happens. It might be minutes, hours, days, or even longer. But, if you can locate the point in time before any of the drama plays out, the Child will be feeling okay.

Nothing bad will have happened, so the Child will be feeling good about himself, happy, content, and completely unaware of what's about to unfold. Here, you need to be watchful for contamination. Young children don't have the ability to experience more than one emotion at a time. The ability to experience mixed feelings comes with emotional maturity. If you want accurate information, make sure you're speaking to the Child.

If the client is reporting mixed feelings or anticipatory fear prior to the event, that fear is either coming out of an earlier event, or it's coming from the Adult Consciousness. Often, it's the Adult Consciousness stepping in. If so, remind the client that "that Part" of them needs to take a back seat.

If the Child is experiencing anticipatory fear, you're not at the ISE. Bridge back to where the Child is still feeling safe and secure. Then progress until the client bumps into the feeling.

#4. The SEAL Pattern

It's possible for a client to land in an event before age 5, report that the feeling is new, be feeling safe and secure before any of the action plays out, and *still* be in an SSE. Frustrating, I know. But don't worry. There is one more test that, when combined with these other tests, gives you a reliable way to verify that you have located an ISE.

The signature of the ISE is what I call the SEAL Pattern. This acronym defines the four aspects that you need to watch for when you're doing the uncovering work: S.E.A.L. for Shock, Energy, Alone, and Lack.

S stands for Shock. An ISE is always an event that begins with a shock or a surprise. Remember – it's new. Something happens. It happens suddenly. The Child doesn't see it coming. And because it's unexpected, it sends a shock through the nervous system of the body. Before this, the Child is feeling safe and secure. All is well in the world. A Child will simply be okay. An infant will be in a very relaxed, diffused state of awareness. Then WHAM! Something happens to change all that.

That's the precise moment the ISE occurs. The shock locks in attention, focusing it on what's happening NOW. The shock is like a ZZT! that ripples through the nervous system of the body. This is a normal, biological response to something unexpected happening. The problem is that any perception of threat is going to generate a stress response in the body. This causes the body to be flooded with stress hormones, like adrenalin and cortisol, that put the body on red-alert.

Stress hormones don't feel good. They generate tension in the body. It doesn't even have to be an actual threat. The Subconscious Mind makes no distinction between real and imagined. If it feels real, then it must be real. The shock makes it a very real threat. And because this event never got resolved, the client has been stuck in that experience ever since. The key to healing this lies in releasing the energy of the event.

E stands for Energy. As soon as you release the initial shock, the Mindbody system will start to relax. It's like holding your breath. The moment you release the breath, you're going to feel better. The release puts an end to the problem.

While there can be multiple aspects contributing to the whole problem, it's that initial shock to the system that gets the ball rolling. And because the ISE is an event that's not over yet, the Subconscious Mind continues to hold onto it *as if* it was a real and present danger. This leaves the client suspended in the energy of a past event, still reliving the thoughts, feelings, and responses, including all the internal stress and tension associated with that experience.

Because the situation hasn't been brought to resolution yet, every time something happens to remind the client of that situation, they get triggered. You know this. When a person gets triggered, they relive the event – either consciously or unconsciously – and the stress response keeps getting activated, over and over again, which just compounds the problem.

The energy trapped in the event is too much for the nervous system of the Child to handle. It feels overwhelming to the Child. As a result, it's interpreted as a threat. Any perception of threat will generate fear. Fear is what tells us to get ourselves to safety – now!

Fear is an emotion. And emotions don't just come out of nowhere. But what's happening is a Story that is based on the perceptions of the Child. This is the information you need to uncover to clear the ISE. What is the Child seeing, hearing, smelling, tasting, feeling? What does that make him think? How is the Child interpreting what's happening? How does that make him feel? What's the specific *thought* responsible for generating that emotion?

The devil is in the details! Behind the emotions, there's a thought. That's the cause of the emotion. For example, a client regresses back into an event in childhood. The uncovering procedure reveals that what was happening was that Mom was distracted by the demands of having too many children. (The client grew up with 12 siblings.) Being the baby meant that her needs were not always met quickly or adequately. As a result, the Child came to the conclusion, *I'm not wanted.* That's a decision of Mind.

What followed was a cascade of thoughts and feelings associated with the event. The thought, *I'm not wanted* generated a feeling of sadness. This generated another thought based on the logic of a Child *If I'm not wanted . . . I won't survive,* which generated intense fear. This is often how an event will play out. It unfolds in layers, much of which is based on a misperception.

The truth is, she was wanted. The fact is, she did survive. But her Subconscious Mind didn't know this because, Subconsciously, there was a Part of her still stuck in that event, still trying to get her needs met. All that was needed was to bring in Adult Consciousness to reality-check each of these thoughts. Recognizing the errors of perception automatically released the uncomfortable feelings and the false beliefs associated with them.

Fear is the mother of all negative emotions. Fear always has to do with the uncertainty of a situation. It's about not being able to *predict* what might happen. If you can't predict what's going to happen in your environment, you don't know how to respond to take care of yourself. If you don't know how to meet your own needs, you won't survive!

A stands for Alone. A Child is dependent on others to take care of his needs. A Child relies on others to help make sense of what's happening in his environment. And when there's no one there to do that, the Child has to deal with it alone. When there is no one there to provide support, the Child becomes acutely aware of just how *alone* they are.

This isn't necessarily a fact, however. Sometimes the Child will tell you that they're alone when, in fact, there are other people present in the scene. What he's telling you is not about being alone. It's about the profound feeling of *isolation* he's experiencing. This reinforces just how *vulnerable* the Child really is, which amplifies the fear and distress.

L stands for Lack. Even if there are others present in that situation, the Child is having to deal with a situation without support. And they lack the resources to be able to do that. The Child is having to deal with all that intensity alone, and they again lack the resources to be able to do that. This realization will then generate a whole cascade of negative thoughts and feelings, many of which will be erroneous.

This is the stuff you need to clear in the ISE because that's what's at the root of the problem. It's not what happened. It's how the Child is interpreting what's happening and the fact that the Child lacks the resources to be able to cope with the situation. It's all just too much for the Child. This is why we bring in Adult Consciousness to support the Child.

Bringing in Adult Consciousness resolves the problem of having to deal with things alone. And whatever resources the Child lacks can be provided by the Adult. This is essentially what Inner Child Work is all about. You are uncovering the underlying cause of the problem so that you can bring the client's Adult Wisdom into the event to provide what was missing the first time.

The underlying problem has to do with a lack of ability to meet one's own needs. That's what you're looking for. What's the unmet need of the Child? Usually, it has to do with either a need for safety or love. If the Child doesn't feel safe for some reason, then what's needed is support and protection. If the Child is feeling abandoned, then what's needed is essentially love and approval. If the Child is feeling overstimulated because of what's happening, then what they need is reassurance that it's not going to last, that they're going to make it through. This is an experience that can be used to develop resilience.

The Child just needs to know that they will survive.

Everything the client needs to be free of the past is already within him. It's in them now. All you have to do is help him gain access to those things, and the healing will happen. Find out what specific needs didn't get met in the ISE. What was missing the first time? Identify the lack. Once you have identified what this unmet need is, you can come up with a way to meet it.

Remember, the Child is helpless. When there is no one there to provide support or help them make sense of things, it reinforces just how powerless and helpless, and vulnerable they really are in that situation. This is what shapes Victim Identity. Victim Identity thinks, *I can't because . . . I'm not strong enough . . . or smart enough . . . or good enough . . . or capable enough.*

These are the thoughts of *the Child*. Thoughts become beliefs. If the Child is experiencing a lack of support, or neglect, or emotional distancing, or abuse, this is contributing to the client's self-image. It's true that the Child does not have the ability to meet important needs. It's true that the Child does not have the wisdom, or the maturity, to make sense of everything that happens. But Adult Consciousness does.

It's just that the Child is dependent on others to meet these needs. And, for whatever reason, that didn't happen. As a result, the Child experienced trauma. Trauma is the perception of threat while in a state of helplessness. It doesn't have to be based on truth or fact. It's just how the situation is being interpreted at that time, based on the maturity of the Child. So, what does the Child need? What's missing?

What's the lack?

Herein lies the key to resolving the problem. Is it a lack of power? A lack of knowledge or understanding? A lack of safety or security? A lack of support? What's missing that the Child needs to be able to get through that situation without being traumatized by it? If you can find a way to meet these needs, you will transform the client's life for the better, and in ways you never imagined. Watch for the SEAL Pattern because this is what *seals* a traumatic experience into memory.

The specific aspects that are contributing to the problem will be unique to each client, based on their history. But an ISE in childhood is always going to be marked by these four aspects:

1. Sudden shock, or surprise
2. Energy intensity
3. Alone in the face of a perceived threat
4. Lack of ability to meet important needs in that moment

Summary

The goal is to locate the ISE and resolve the client's issue where it got started. If you instruct the client back to an earlier event, you'll find it much easier to Bridge back to the ISE. You can just hop from one lily-pad to the next, all the way back to the ISE. It might take you two or three hops. It might take many more. Just let the Subconscious Mind lead the way to what's calling for resolution.

When you land in an event, do a little preliminary uncovering, then test for the ISE. The goal is to get to the ISE. Continue bridging back until you find it!

There are multiple ways to test for the ISE, including:

1. The Age Test
2. The Feeling Test
3. The Safety Test
4. The SEAL Pattern

The uncovering procedure begins with the moment of shock/surprise. Events tend to follow a bell-curve and come to a peak. There can be layers of perceptions and thoughts and feelings trapped in the event. You need to grind down to the underlying root cause by rewinding and replaying the event multiple times. Releasing trapped emotions will give you access to these deeper layers of information.

Learn more in the Root Cause Remedy for Results Course here: www.tribeofhealers.com/root-cause-remedy-for-results-course

My life has a superb cast, but I cannot figure out the plot. –
Ashleigh Brilliant

CHAPTER 13:
Uncover the Story

Everybody has a story that could break your heart. - **Amanda Marshall**

In his youth, the Fisher King was out playing in the woods. He stumbled upon a camp where he found a fire with a salmon cooking over it. The lad was young, hungry, and seeing that no one was about, he reached out to take some of the salmon. The fish was too hot to handle, however, and burned his fingers. He immediately dropped the salmon and put his fingers in his mouth - just as the owners of the camp returned.

There are several variations on what follows, but the story always ends in the Grail Castle, where life for the adult King has become simply unbearable. He's in constant agony. Only one thing distracts him from his chronic state of suffering – fishing.

Ironically, the Fisher King's castle is the keeper of the Holy Grail, which is said to have the power to heal all wounds. Every night there is a wonderful procession that brings forth the Grail. Each and every person in the royal assemblage of the castle instantly receives what he wishes from the Grail. Everyone, that is, except the Fisher King. The King is unable to accept the healing because the ISE prevents him from accepting the healing. There's a block.

The Fisher King story contains some clear indicators that the event in childhood could be the ISE. First, the story begins with the boy playing in the woods, where he is feeling safe and secure. Second, the boy is young. An ISE can occur at almost any age but most often occurs before the formation of the Critical Function around age 5 or 6. Third, the boy is hungry, indicating an unmet need. This need stimulates a searching behavior. The boy finds the salmon on the spit, and, like an infant, he reaches out for it. This is the turning point in the story. Had the salmon been merely warm, the boy's need would have been satisfied. He would have experienced pleasure and satisfaction and probably wandered off to have a nap. Rest and relaxation indicate the completion of a normal/healthy circuit.

But that's not what happens in the story. The salmon is too hot, indicating an overwhelmingly uncomfortable feeling (physical or emotional pain). Automatically the boy moves to stop the feeling by putting his fingers in his mouth. At the very same moment, the owners of the camp return. That's the moment of wounding. The moment the boy stops the feeling from being fully felt and expressed (i.e., represses), he's caught red-handed with life-long consequences. The cycle of suffering begins.

From now on, every time the boy is confronted by a situation that, in any way, reminds him of the initial event that sensitized him, his Subconscious Mind will perceive a threat. And the body will naturally generate tension in anticipation of injury. This susceptibility to cramps or clamping down will lead to attempts to either avoid pain or achieve satisfaction, either through acting out (e.g., panic attacks) or substitute needs (e.g., smoking). As the tension mounts, it becomes a self-punishment program leading to the final stage of fear and anger/hatred, which "also includes despair, resignation, sorrow, exhaustion, rage, and the like."

Unconscious fear is always the fruit of injury. - **Konrad Stettbacher**

The Seed Planting Event

The Initial Sensitizing Event (ISE) is the seed-planting event. Subsequent Sensitizing Events (SSE) are ensuing circumstances, situations, or events that, in some way, resonate with the ISE. Because the Mind works through association, any sensory input – for example, the taste of salmon, the forest, horses, fire, etc. - can serve to reinforce the perceptions, thoughts, and feelings established in the ISE.

Intensity and repetition of SSEs determine how quickly a problem will become evident. A mild upset might take years of compounding before any symptoms appear. A severe trauma, on the other hand, will require very little reinforcement. It's just a matter of stacking up enough bricks in the wall. Then, all it takes is one more SSE and POOF! The feeling finds its way to the surface in the form of symptoms.

By middle life, much of our feeling life is wounded. Another perspective yields a startling survey of wounded feelings. Anything that is put back into the unconscious (as when the fisher king drops the salmon that he has just picked up) once it has been in consciousness turns dark and becomes a symptom in one's psychological structure. - Robert Johnson

The Grail Procession is like a series of SSEs. Each event presents an opportunity for healing. But the Fisher King is trapped in the cycle of unconscious suffering, habitually fishing for external solutions to an inner problem. Until he takes the lid off and looks inside, he will be unable to partake of the Grail's healing powers.

In the Grail Myth, the key to healing lies in answering the question. *What ails thee?* The Conscious Mind thinks that the symptoms are the problem. This is why every attempt at an external solution has failed to resolve the problem. Remember the soldier's first meeting with the devil? The question, *What ails thee? Why do you look so unhappy?* is bringing attention to the physical or emotional pain, discomfort, or trouble. But the devil recognizes that symptom is a signal coming out of the event that caused it.

With regression hypnotherapy, everything pivots on finding and releasing the energies trapped in the causal event (ISE). This is why you must test for the ISE. The ISE is the source of the Symptom Imperative. The key to healing lies in the ISE. Secondary events (SSE) rest upon the ISE, so they cannot stand on their own. Removing the ISE's influence causes the entire structure to collapse like a house of cards. But it's also possible to neutralize a problem by extinguishing key SSEs.

As every SSE rests upon the preceding layer, every time you remove an SSE, it weakens the entire structure supporting it. Theoretically, at least, if you release enough SSEs, the whole structure should crumble, putting an end to unwanted symptoms. It just takes more time. Even if the ISE remains on its own, it has insufficient power to generate symptoms. Without the wall, it's just a brick. The underlying problem could simply remain dormant, having no further effect in the client's life. And if it took 40 years to build up enough steam for symptoms to come to the surface, it might take another 40 years to accumulate enough SSEs to result in a recurrence of symptoms.

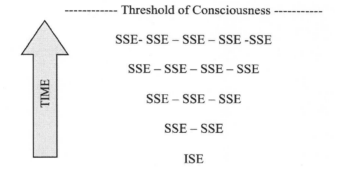

SYMPTOMS (Physical, Mental, Emotional) **EMERGE**

SPE

------------ Threshold of Consciousness -----------

SSE- SSE – SSE – SSE -SSE

SSE – SSE – SSE – SSE

SSE – SSE – SSE

SSE – SSE

ISE

The Symptom Producing Event (SPE) is at the threshold of consciousness. This is an event the client usually has a conscious memory of. For example, the first time he had a panic attack, or smoked a cigarette, or binged on ice-cream. This is not the ISE, however. The SPE is the first time the Subconscious Mind found a solution to the problem by expressing through symptoms. Treating the SPE will not resolve the problem because the root of the problem lies in an earlier life experience.

While resolving the SPE can produce temporary results, as the triggering event continues to occur, the panic attacks will soon return. The client will start smoking again. He'll go on an eating binge or a drinking bender. The rash will reappear. The cancer will return. It's only a matter of time before the symptoms will recur.

To resolve the problem for good, you must identify what happened to necessitate symptoms in the first place. What is the Symptom Imperative? To uncover this, the event must be viewed through the eyes of the Child. This is because the problem is not what happened. It's not what was said or done or how those things made the client feel. The problem has to do with how the experience was interpreted at that time. This has everything to do with the age at which it occurred.

When an event is left unresolved, it's because whatever was happening was being perceived through a consciousness that lacked either the maturity or the resources needed to be able to cope with the situation. This generated uncomfortable feelings and emotions. That's what makes any event memorable - how it feels.

Emotion is the motivating power of the Subconscious Mind. This is what drives behavior. If you're dealing with an unwanted habitual behavior like smoking, overeating, drinking, etc., look for an uncomfortable feeling that comes on just before the client reaches for the substance of choice. The feeling is not the problem. What *causes* an emotion is a Thought.

Feelings don't come out of nowhere. The underlying cause of the problem has to do with decisions that are being made during an emotionally-charged life experience. This is what Stephen Parkhill called Thought-Cause Alignment. *This* is what you're looking for during the uncovering procedure.

Thought-Cause Alignment

Affect Bridge is a process of following that emotion back to its birthplace. The ISE is the seed-planting event for a specific emotion. The uncovering procedure which follows allows you to discover what happened to cause that feeling. To do this, you must first help the client to step fully into the event and revivify the event. But you are entering forbidden territory and asking the client to bring to consciousness information that has been hidden from awareness. To gain access to the underlying cause of the problem, you must carefully tease out all the details regarding the who, what, when, where, and how of that life experience.

The uncovering procedure is a repetitive process because there can be multiple layers of perceptions, thoughts, and feelings. For example, the feeling you Bridged back on might have been fear. But if you dig a little deeper, you may discover a deeper layer. It might be anger, or it could be a deeper fear. That's the root cause - that fear. But to get to *that* fear, you need to clear all the layers.

You need to clean house. The way to do this is to simply keep rewinding and replaying the event until everything has been neutralized. Your initial uncovering will only bring to light the surface layer of information about what happened. Releasing the emotions trapped at that layer will give you access to the deeper layer. That's basically all there is to it. Rewind. Review. Release. Repeat. Some people call this process of grinding down to the root cause peeling the onion.

Picture an event as a bell-curve. This arc has a beginning, which rises to a peak, then falls off towards the end. The beginning is the moment of shock or surprise. This is when the Child realizes, *Uh-oh! I'm in trouble!* The end hasn't happened yet. That's the problem. The situation was left hanging. Subconsciously, the event is still active. Your job is to bring it to an end.

The middle is where all the action happens. This is where the uncovering work is focused. Your objective is to clean house by identifying all the aspects contributing to the problem. These include perceptions, physical sensations, thoughts, and decisions.

Sensory Perceptions

Our ability to recognize patterns is how we survived as a species. What matters most is first impressions because these are direct downloads stored for future reference. The first impressions regarding an event are sensory perceptions. What is the Child seeing, hearing, smelling, tasting, feeling? For example, hot/cold, soft/hard, loud/soft, bright/dark, comfortable/uncomfortable, etc.

Anything that's being perceived can establish an anchor. When sufficiently reinforced, it becomes a trigger for unwanted responses. This serves the function of survival, but it can establish irrational fears and responses later in life. For example, I had a client who developed an allergy to a song. No kidding. If you put your hand on a hot stove, your Subconscious Mind is going to protect you from it in the future. Hence the saying, "once burned, twice shy!" This is the basis of a phobia.

Sensory information from external circumstances generates a response in the body. The body really only has two states; either contracted or relaxed, comfortable, or uncomfortable. Hunger, for example, is a feeling of contraction or pain. For an infant, this is a full-body experience that sets off a red-alert. As soon as the need for food is met, the baby feels pleasure, and the body relaxes again.

Thoughts

External stimuli are being evaluated and assigned meaning. This is a Thought. It is a decision of Mind based on how the Child feels. Pleasure, comfort, and relaxation feel "good." Contraction, discomfort, and pain feel *bad*.

Thoughts form the basis of beliefs. Core Beliefs are formed very early in life and have to do with identity, relationships, and what to expect from life in the future. These Thoughts include:

- I am

- They are

- The world/life is

Note: An infant's first response to uncomfortable physical sensations is often confusion. This can actually be an indication that you have located the ISE. The Child doesn't know what to make of what's happening because it's a new experience.

Emotions

Thoughts generate emotions. A good experience will be reflected in positive thoughts, which will generate pleasant emotions like happiness, curiosity, okay-ness. A bad experience will generate negative thoughts, resulting in uncomfortable emotions like fear, anger, sadness.

The emotional response is based on how the situation is being interpreted by the Child at that time. This is a key understanding to grasp. The emotion is not irrational. It is congruent with the Thought.

Emotions are felt physically in the body. Normally, as soon as the stimulus is no longer present, the feeling will quickly subside. These physical sensations don't last very long. But when an emotion has a lid put on it, holding it down, the feeling stays stuck inside. With nowhere to go, it is available for re-triggering by similar situations.

Subsequent Sensitizing Events (SSE) cause the Subconscious Mind to recycle the original event in an attempt to come up with a solution to the problem. The problem is that it can't because it only has the maturity and resources of the Child at the age at which the event occurred. This keeps the person stuck in the fears and misperceptions of childhood.

Unresolved emotions can be triggered by external or internal stimuli. For example, a panic attack can be triggered merely by thinking about snakes. The Thought triggers the biology of fear with muscle contraction, dryness in the mouth, a racing heart, etc. And any event of triggering, whether consciously or unconsciously, will have a compounding effect, causing the unresolved pattern of thoughts, feelings, and emotions held within the ISE to grow stronger.

Action/Re-Action

Emotion is the motivating energy of the Subconscious Mind. This is what spurs us on to ensure that we take action to meet our needs: E-Motion. For example, an experience of loss will generate the emotion of sadness. Sadness motivates us to find another way to meet whatever need was created by the loss. It might be a need for companionship, creativity, or comfort or something else. But the feeling is not the problem. The Thought behind the sadness will tell you what the real problem is.

Anger indicates a need for boundaries. It motivates us to protect ourselves and the things that are important to us. Anger can also point to an injustice, a hurt, or a sense of unfairness that needs to be corrected. But anger is not the problem. The Thought behind the anger will tell you what (and who) the real problem is.

Emotions just don't come out of nowhere. The emotion is there to motivate some kind of action. But always, the Emotion is preceded by a Thought. That is the cause you are looking for. For example, the Thought, *I'm going to die!* is a decision of Mind that the situation is one of threat. This thought will generate the Emotion of fear. Confusion will generate fear because not knowing how to respond to take care of your needs is a threat to survival. Fear is supposed to get us running to safety or defending ourselves. That's good.

Understanding this fundamental relationship between Thought and Emotion will transform your sessions. Thoughts generate emotions that drive behavior. Unconsciously-driven actions based in unresolved past experiences become habituated over time. They take the form of behaviors and re-actions which find expression through symptoms. Symptoms such as weight gain, diabetes, joint pain, anxiety, etc. are not the problem. The problem has to do with a Thought.

While the Conscious Mind can choose, the Subconscious Mind decides. It's all based on past experiences. The Subconscious Mind doesn't think. It just runs the programming it has stored in memory. These programs are emotional in nature and can be identified through Thought-Cause Alignment.

Thought-Cause Alignment is a Stimulus-Response pattern. It begins with a Stimulus Sensory Perception, which stimulates Physical Sensations. The cause of physical sensations of tension or contraction is a specific perception – seeing, hearing, smelling, tasting, touching – which can seed an anchor. The felt-experience is interpreted and finds expression as a Thought.

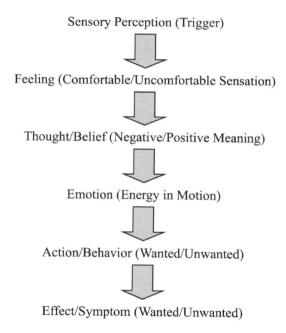

Sensory Perception (Trigger)

Feeling (Comfortable/Uncomfortable Sensation)

Thought/Belief (Negative/Positive Meaning)

Emotion (Energy in Motion)

Action/Behavior (Wanted/Unwanted)

Effect/Symptom (Wanted/Unwanted)

The cause of the Thought is the discomfort being experienced. The meaning being assigned to what's happening will then generate an Emotion like fear, anger, or sadness. The Emotion is always congruent with and caused by the Thought. The Emotion motivates action in order to meet the specific need being expressed by the Thought. For example, safety, nourishment, achievement, connection, etc. The action (or inability to take action) in the ISE then gets reinforced by SSEs, causing symptoms.

This is the information to make a note of during the uncovering procedure. It represents the Symptom Producing Pattern calling for resolution.

- Perception (seeing, hearing, smelling, tasting, touching)

- Sensation (comfortable or uncomfortable)

- Thought (about self, other, what might happen)

- Emotion (fear, anger, sadness, etc.)

- Action (fight, flee, freeze, cry, etc.)

Session Mapping

Following a feeling back into earlier and earlier events can make it easier to locate the ISE. Regression hypnotherapy is not just about finding the ISE and fixing it, however. You need the larger Story, which is made up of a sequence of SSEs. Creating a Session Map will give you something to refer to as you guide the client back into earlier and earlier events. It also produces an inventory of SSEs. You'll need these later to test and compound all changes during the Verification Phase.

For practical purposes, we can picture a person's timeline as a linear set of railway tracks. We can imagine leaving the train station in the Here and Now, tracking back to earlier and earlier events which go all the way back to the causal event. The process that allows us to move along this imaginary timeline is called a Bridge. The Subconscious Mind is not linear, however.

What you're dealing with is a matrix of events that are all connected by the same thread. We can access any event simply by following the thread back to its inception because, as far as the Subconscious Mind is concerned, everything is happening NOW, NOW, NOW. This is what makes regression possible. A more appropriate model for the Subconscious Mind would be a spider's web. The stronger the thread, the more access you have to the events that are feeding into the client's issue. This is because they're all transmitting the same signal simultaneously. Regression is simply following the thread of a thought, physical sensation, or emotion.

To create a Session Map, draw a horizontal line on a sheet of paper. Divide this line into three sections. The first section begins on the far left and pertains to pre-natal events. Write the number zero here to indicate Conception.

The second section is where you will keep track of life events from birth until Now. This comprises the largest section of your timeline map. At the beginning of the second section, write B to signify Birth.

The beginning of the third section signifies the starting point of your regression, which may be the moment Now or a recent triggering event. Beyond this lies future events. This gives you a visual map to follow that gives you the Story about the growth and development of the client's issue.

As the client Bridges back into earlier and earlier events, you can make a note of the key information, including Age, Perceptions, Thoughts, Emotions. Once you have the key information about the event, conduct the test for the ISE and continue bridging back until you find it.

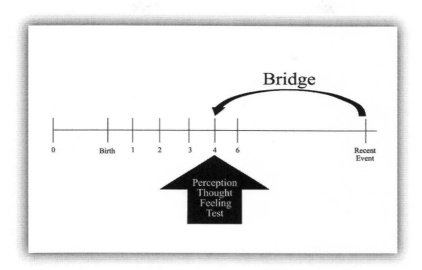

Age: How young is the client in the event? The Age Test tells us that the ISE is usually going to be some time before the age of five. Unless there is a specific traumatic event later in life, events that occurred before age five are the ones to which to give attention.

Perceptions: Perceptions have to do with *what's happening* in the event. What is the Child seeing, hearing, smelling, tasting, and feeling that's significant to the feeling you Bridged back on? These could be anchors that will need to be removed. For example, *the look on his face, the smell of alcohol, that song,* etc.

Thoughts: How is the client *interpreting* what's happening in that event? What does that make them think? Children routinely misinterpret things so, once you have located the ISE, you need to reality-check any Thoughts with the client's *Adult* Consciousness. For example, if the Child says, *I'm not wanted*, that's a Thought that may or may not be true.

The Child is making a decision that says, *I am a person who is not wanted* (or worthy, or deserving). You need to reality check that by asking Adult Consciousness, *Is that true?* because there's no such thing as a neutral thought. And when a Thought goes unchallenged, it can form a belief. The question is - What's happening to make the Child think, *I'm not wanted?*

The only way to know if a Thought is true is to check with the Adult. Is that true? Is he not wanted? Remember, Core Beliefs are shaped by events in childhood. They decide what we're going to get in life. The Child lacks the maturity to make sense of what's happening and can misinterpret meaning. Adult Consciousness can correct these errors in perception. And changing these erroneous beliefs can have a dramatic impact on a person's life.

Sometimes, however, the Child is interpreting what's happening correctly. In this case, Adult Consciousness' job is to help the Child accept the truth and release the emotional charge. This frees the Child to grow up into adulthood, transforming how the client thinks and feels in daily life.

Emotions: How the Child is interpreting what's happening in the event? Thoughts generate emotions. The specific Thought will determine the specific emotion calling for expression. Remember, the emotion isn't the problem. The purpose of the emotion is to motivate the client to take action and meet an important need. The question is - What need isn't being met? What's the Lack? What does the Child want or need? This is the key to resolving the underlying problem.

Mapping your regression sessions along a visual timeline can help you to develop your skill at facilitating the healing process of regression hypnotherapy. Not only will this give you a way to make a note of the critical information like age, perceptions, decisions, and emotions, but as you track these things, you'll begin to notice patterns.

This can provide insight into the overall pattern, the Matrix, which will help you to guide the healing process and resolve the whole problem. For example, if you're following the feeling of fear, you may notice that it's always the same Thought. Or the feeling is always showing up in the gut. Or it involves the same people, color, smell, etc. It may just be the same Story playing out, over and over, again.

Because the Mind works through association, more than one event or player can be involved in a condition. Newer memories build upon older memories, all the way back to childhood. The Subconscious Mind will naturally want to associate with other events in a bid to get more relief. The problem is that the Subconscious Mind tends to lump all kinds of memories together. What we want to do is separate them and work on them one at a time. Success lies in thoroughly collapsing the emotional connection to each event *before* shifting to other scenes or events.

Summary

Affect Bridge is a process of following the feeling back into the event that caused it. The feeling is not the cause of the problem, however. The problem has to do with the thought behind the feeling. This is Thought-Cause Alignment. Thoughts generate emotions that motivate us to take action to meet our needs. The goal of the uncovering procedure in the ISE is to uncovering what specific needs of the Child are not being met.

Mapping your session along an imaginary timeline can help you to organize events in a linear fashion, making it easier to track the overall

Story of how the problem developed over time. Your Session Map can help you to identify the overall pattern while uncovering the specific aspects that are calling for resolution. Once you have cleared all the aspects trapped in the ISE, you'll have a record of everything you need for the Verification Phase, where you will make all positive changes permanent.

Learn more in the Ready for Regression First Session System Course here: www.tribeofhealers.com/ready-for-regression-first-session-system-course

CHAPTER 14:
Parts Work

*E*verything we have is a resource, but some people do not
perceive parts of themselves this way. As long as we have
to put down, hide, reject, or deny anything about ourselves,
we cannot use our energy freely. - **The Satir Model**

Parts Work or Parts Therapy is really a foundation for effective
regression hypnotherapy. Parts are aspects of the personality that are
either calling for healing, or that can assist us in doing the healing work.
Inner Child Work involves uncovering, identifying, and healing
disowned or wounded Child Parts.

Inner Child Work is central to the work of regression hypnotherapy
because Child Parts are feeling Parts. They are shaped by events very
early in life and form our Core Beliefs. Each Part has its own memories
and individual point of view, based on past experiences and what was
learned from them. As such, it can be a source of empowerment or a
problem depending on how it's expressing in a person's life.

Parts express as symptoms. They express as thoughts and feelings, and behaviors. They show up as unwanted reactions and physical conditions, including disease. Many of the problems that clients come to you for help with have to do with Parts that are out of alignment with the client's conscious wishes. For example, clients will come to you for help in resolving habitual patterns of negative self-talk, painful emotions, uncontrollable reactions, and irrational behaviors that were seeded in experiences that occurred in childhood.

Sigmund Freud recognized that many of our Parts are formed during childhood and can make themselves known through dreams and hypnosis. He theorized that childhood memories can be repressed and that repressed Parts express as unconscious drives, which can cause problems in adult life. For example, instinctive and primitive drives for self-preservation and procreation are responsible for unconscious behaviors.

Carl Jung, a student of Freud, originated the concept of an Inner Child. This has been expanded upon by many different therapies. For example, Fritz Perl's Gestalt Therapy works with Parts. Hypnotherapy calls this Chair Therapy or dialogue work. Virginia Satir developed a method for working with multiple Parts at the same time called the Parts Party. In hypnotherapy, this is called the Conference Room Technique.

According to poet Robert Bly, Parts of the personality are like a platoon. When one Part is executive, it acts like a sergeant, making commitments. Unfortunately, this occurs without consulting the platoon, which can result in internal conflicts. The process of bringing Parts back into alignment is what Fritz Perls called the gestalt.

Gestalt, which means *the whole that is greater than the sum of its Parts,* is rooted in the idea that we are not just one person; we're more like a community of Parts. Every Part of a community has a specific role or job, which serves an important function in service to the whole personality. This means that every Part is a valuable contributor to the whole. Some Parts may behave badly, but every Part serves a positive purpose. And when all Parts are working together in harmony, we experience an internal state of well-being, we're more resourceful and enjoy greater health and happiness in daily life.

We have many, many Parts that, together, make up the personality. These can include Offender Parts, Malicious Parts, Body Parts, Spiritual Parts, Habitual Parts, and more. While any of these Parts can be accessed through hypnosis, the three primary Parts we work with in regression sessions are:

1. The Inner Child
2. The Adult or Grownup Part
3. Parent Parts

As far as the Subconscious Mind is concerned, we're not just one person. We're more of a kaleidoscope of Parts. These Parts of the self were all shaped by specific experiences growing up, and they're still there, held within the Subconscious level of Mind. As a result, the grownup client sitting in your chair is, at some level, still a teenager. They have toddlers and infants alive inside of them, vying for attention. There's even a Part of them that is still inside Mom!

If you're not trained in Parts Therapy, I have a few book suggestions for you. *The Satir Method* by Virginia Satir is an easy read and highly relevant to regression hypnotherapy. *I'm Okay – You're Okay* by

Thomas Harris will teach you about the three primary Parts we work with – Child, Parent, Adult – while providing insight into the developmental stages of childhood.

Parts are also known as *Ego States* or subpersonalities. Ego States by John and Helen Watkins is based on a research project at Stanford University that offers great insights into the whole concept of Parts and multiple personalities (Dissociative Identity Disorder.) *Ego Therapy by* Gordon Emerson is another worthy read.

Charles Tebbetts took Paul Federn's approach to working with ego parts and adapted it to hypnotherapy. Roy Hunter was mentored by Charles Tebbetts. His book *Hypnosis for Inner Conflict Resolution is a comprehensive* text on Parts Therapy written specifically for hypnosis practitioners.

Inner Child Parts

While Parts can be formed at any age, the most significant ones are shaped in childhood. Child Parts are recordings of learned responses to specific experiences in childhood. There's not just one Inner Child, however. We have many, many Inner Child Parts. Each is a recording of an actual event and contains the perceptions, thoughts, and feelings of the Child at the age at which it was formed.

As the Critical Faculty of the Mind isn't fully formed until around age 6, Parts which formed prior to this time contribute to shaping a person's identity. The younger the Child, is the more hyper-receptive they are to verbal and non-verbal suggestions, particularly those coming from the Parents. Most of the issues you'll work with will track back to early childhood.

Inner Child Parts can have a lasting impact on a person's life because they're responsible for Core Beliefs and primary emotions like fear, sadness, anger, and hurt. Core Beliefs form the Critical Faculty of the Mind, which decides what we're going to get in life, based on our past experiences.

When you regress a client to an event in childhood, the Child is a recording of how the client was experiencing that particular situation. Something was happening to cause that Part to form in the first place. The Part is expressing an emotional response to something that was being said or done, seen, or heard *at that time*. It is an echo from the past.

Problem-generating Parts are often Child Parts that have been judged and rejected for not being "good enough." This creates an internal conflict because Enough-ness is our natural state. So, look for the Lack. Identify what specifically was needed by the Child in that situation. Was it a lack of support? A lack of safety? The inability to make sense of things? How was the Child making sense of what was happening? What was the Thought?

Typically, it will be a Thought of not *enough*. For example,

- I'm not loveable (enough).

- I'm not important (enough).

- I'm not wanted (enough).

- I'm not smart (enough).

- I'm not good (enough).

When Parts express as unwanted symptoms, they are always meant to be helpful. They're pointing to an unmet need at the Subconscious level of Mind. Sometimes the problem is simply that the Child misinterpreted the situation. Sometimes it was due to abuse. Mostly, it's because the Child was feeling overwhelmed.

When a Child feels overwhelmed and there's no one there to provide support, the Child has to figure out how to cope with the situation on its own. A strategy that worked well for a toddler, however, may not be working so well for the client as an adult. Responses formed in childhood will be viewed by Adult Consciousness as irrational or out of control. Because the Conscious Mind needs a sense of control, the tendency will be to put a lid on the memory.

When we repress a Part of ourselves, it cannot grow up. A Part that has been denied, rejected, judged, or condemned stays stuck in the formative event. That's the ISE. From there, it will continue to strive for recognition through symptoms. Parts can wreak havoc by enslaving a person to inhibitions or drives to excess. Emotional problems like insecurity, self-doubt, anxiety, addiction, social impairment, and even diseases are often rooted in patterns that develop as a result of experiences in childhood. But the Child is never the problem. It's what is calling for healing.

What we resist persists. – **Carl Jung**

The Adult Part

The Adult Part is responsible for healing the Child Parts. All healing is self-healing. It's by loving and accepting the Child that the Adult installs the inner security, self-worth, and confidence needed to take appropriate action in the future. The Adult Part is essentially the

Conscious Mind of the client in the here and now. This Part relies on thinking, reasoning, and logic. It's the Grownup Part of the client that has the ability to analyze, evaluate and apply Adult Wisdom.

The Adult Part is very important to regression hypnosis because this is the Part of the client that has the capacity for insight and realization. It's the Grownup Mind. Remember, the rings of the tree Mind Model? The Subconscious Mind is simply the Conscious Mind of the past. When you go back to an event in childhood, you are going back to the Child Mind. You are accessing the ring of the tree that was exposed to the outer world *at that time.*

The events held within each ring represent the Conscious Mind of the client *at that age.* If you go back to an event at two-years-old, the Conscious Mind of the client has only the maturity and understanding of a two-year-old. This is the consciousness that was available at that time.

When the Mind is very young, it is highly impressionable. Small things can make a big impression. When a child gets hurt, or is unable to communicate an important need, or can't make sense of what's going on in his environment, or can't control what's happening, it creates a conflict in the Mind. To survive, a child must learn to adapt by growing around painful experiences.

This does not mean that the client has to suffer for the rest of his life, however. Unlike the Child, the Adult Part of the client has developed cognitive and emotional maturity. They have more life experience to draw from. As a result, Adult understanding can be brought into a painful past event to review, reevaluate and reality-check perceptions, discover connections, and see the bigger picture. This creates the conditions where newer, better decisions can be made to allow healing to happen.

Internal Parent Parts

The Parent who shows up in a regression session is not the actual parent. It is an Internal Representation of how the client perceived his parent as a child. It is a Part of the client. Parent Parts are recordings of the impressions made on the client by the Parents in childhood. Just as we have more than one Child Part, we have multiple Parent Parts. Each is based on the specific parental impression and the age of the Child. Parent Parts are based on what was modeled in childhood, what was observed, and what was said or done to the Child.

Parents provide both the rules needed to survive and navigate our way through life. The rules tell us how to be and how not be in order to get our needs met. They instill family, cultural and religious values, which are accepted as truths. Parents project onto their children beliefs, values, and expectations. They also provide the *how-tos* of life. How to brush your teeth. How to tie your shoelaces. How to ride a bicycle. How to tell time. They also condition their kids to be competitive or fear others' opinions. What will the neighbors think?

Parents become the voices in our heads. They're the blah-blah-blah that yammers away in the background telling us right from wrong, shoulds, and should-nots. These voices get internalized as Parent Parts. For example, the Inner Critic is often the voice of a Critical Parent Part. This is how perfectionism is learned.

How we parent our own children is often a reflection, or a rejection, of how we were parented as children. Problems in relationships often have to do with a troubled relationship with a parent. Our choices of partners are based on what was modeled to us growing up. When there's conflict in the marriage, taking the mask off the spouse can show you which parental relationship the client is struggling with.

Parts come in all shapes and sizes. There are Child Parts, Parent Parts, Offender Parts, and even malicious Parts that are operating outside of conscious control. The key to helping a Part to heal is recognizing that, no matter how badly that Part may behave, it's not bad. It's just stuck in a bad place.

Nasty Parts

Sharon, a New Age spiritual healer, had wanted to gain insight into the presence of a negative energy that she was sensing in her apartment. This energy really had her freaked out. She was afraid to go to sleep at night and wondered if this energy was attached to her. As Sharon focused on her feelings, a rather nasty *dark* energy was revealed.

In attempting to converse with this Part of the client, I soon discovered that this Part wasn't very forthcoming. It refused to tell me its name. It wouldn't tell me where it came from or who had recruited it. While all Parts are good, not all of them are friendly. Not only was this Part not friendly, it wasn't willing to talk to me. This makes it pretty hard to have a conversation, though. In fact, the only thing I could squeeze out of it was that it had been with Sharon a very long time and that its sole purpose was to make her life miserable.

The more I questioned the Part, the more annoyed and hostile it became toward me. Finally, it asked me a seething question. Do you know who I am?

I decided to play dumb rather than get into a wrestling match with a Part of the client. "No," I replied innocently. *"Why don't you tell me?"*

This seemed to irritate the Part even more. It then hissed back at me, "You're not very smart, are you?" Okay, at least now we were talking. I decided to continue to play dumb and respectfully asked the Part to enlighten me. Honestly, I think it was sheer exasperation that compelled this Part to reveal its identity to me.

What's interesting is that when it revealed its identity, it did so in a hushed tone. Clearly, this Part was *afraid* of getting caught! "Sa-tan," it whispered. "You know –THE DEVIL!"

The client thought she was possessed by a demon! But I was not speaking with an employee of the devil. I was speaking to a frightened Child. I knew that I was dealing with a deeply wounded Part of the client and that it was frustrated with not being able to get an important need met. It wasn't just frustrated anymore. It was angry. VERY angry.

The Core Parts of the personality are shaped during the formative years when a Child is vulnerable. As a result, many Child Parts have a protective function. Some Parts formed as a result of the conditioning process, growing up. Some are due to traumatic experiences. But Parts are recordings of how the person learned to cope with a specific set of circumstances.

Unfortunately, I was still learning how to facilitate regression hypnotherapy and did not have the knowledge or skill needed to deal with this issue. I just did my best to muddle through using a Parts Therapy approach. In fact, it wasn't until after the session that Sharon revealed her history. She had grown up as the daughter of a Baptist preacher and, from the earliest age, had been immersed in fire-and-brimstone guilt and fear. She had been taught to fear the devil.

This was a major contributing factor to forming this Part of her that was so nasty. This malevolent Part of Sharon had been judged, and rejected, and denied in childhood for being bad. That's what evil is, right? Evil is bad. VERY bad. But the religious theme was just a reflection of Sharon's upbringing. This Part of her was carrying a load of guilt and fear so that Sharon wouldn't have to. That's a very loving thing to do, isn't it?

That's what Parts do. They meet needs. In this case, the Part was protecting Sharon, albeit in a very twisted way. But that's how it is with Parts. They are always trying to satisfy an important need for the client based on the wisdom available to them at the age at which they formed. Parts embody decisions that were made earlier in life. While these decisions may have served the client at that time, they can become limitations later in life. The younger the Part is, the less resourceful it will be. And the more vulnerable it feels.

Through the process, I was able to convince Sharon to release the angry Part by generating the feeling of Joy. Essentially, we displaced the negative emotion by generating a much stronger, positive emotion. This created an internal environment that was uncomfortable for the angry Part. As a result, it chose to leave. While this is not the outcome I would aspire to, today, it resolved the problem. At least, temporarily.

Still, I can't help but wonder what might have been revealed if I had simply followed that feeling back to the causal event. This malicious, angry, self-punishing Part of the client was coming out of a past where, as a child, the client was conditioned for guilt and fear. Regression to Cause would have revealed the specific moment in time in which the problem got seeded. It would have brought to light the experience that necessitated the formation of this *demonic* Part of her.

All Parts formed to meet important needs for safety, nourishment, and comfort. Every Part deserves to be treated with kindness and respect. Even angry or malicious Parts. Problem-causing Parts are often a problem because they have been judged and rejected. Angry, destructive Parts are often Child Parts that have been deeply wounded and need to be loved and accepted in order to heal.

The uncovering process of regression hypnotherapy would have allowed Adult Sharon to gain insight into what caused this destructive Part of her to form in the first place. She might have realized how this Part of her was stuck in the past. And how it actually served a positive purpose. Perhaps it formed to protect her by carrying the burden of evil put upon her long before she could think for herself.

Releasing the internal trapped emotions might have brought greater clarity, allowing Sharon deeper wisdom into how negative programming early in life impacts a Child. She might have gained insight into how these false beliefs were conflicting with the deeper truth of her essential goodness. She would have seen, for herself, how this conflict had impacted her growing up, and how it continued to impact her as an adult. These insights and understandings would have allowed Sharon to love and accept this Part of her back to wholeness. Transforming and then integrating this Part as a valuable and worthy part of her whole self would have given her access to new resources and greater empowerment.

Months later, Sharon was still holding onto the positive results. The worthless-sinner-deserving-of-punishment-program that she had struggled with for most of her life was finally gone. But for how long? If I had known then, what I know now, I would have done things differently. Banishing a Part doesn't resolve the problem. If anything, it just drives it deeper underground. Any attempt to amputate a Part is going to make the problem worse.

It's just a matter of time because it starts to reassert itself because, when a wounded Part of a person gets disowned or rejected, it's like banishing it to hell. With nowhere to turn, it can start to take on some nasty qualities. Malevolent Parts can drive a person to act out in self-destructive ways. No question. Sharon's was generating anxiety. It was keeping her awake at night. She was growing more paranoid by the day.

But every Part is a worthy Part of the personality. It's a valuable resource that the client has been cut off from. If it's stuck, it needs to be liberated. The thing to remember is that these Parts need help. The Part generating the problem is not the enemy. It's wounded and stuck. Often, it's a Child Part that's doing its very best to meet an important need for the client.

The problem is that it only has the resources it had at the age it formed. Suppose you're two years -old. In that case, you might learn that sucking your thumb is an effective strategy for soothing yourself whenever you feel anxious. Sucking your thumb when you're two years old is helpful because, when you feel scared or insecure, relief is close at hand. But when you're thirty-two years old, it's an embarrassing habit. Adult thumb-sucking just isn't socially acceptable. It's right up there with nose-picking and farting in public. Plus, thumb sucking can push your teeth out of alignment, and orthodontic work isn't cheap.

When putting your thumb in your mouth becomes a threat, guess what the Subconscious Mind is going to do? Step in to protect. The need for soothing, or security, or whatever need that behavior is satisfying, hasn't gone away. The Subconscious Mind comes up with a more socially acceptable way to satisfy that need. Guess what? Eating and smoking are socially accepted, self-soothing behaviors. That's how you need to think of them.

Sucking on a cigarette is like sucking your thumb. Putting food in your mouth when you're not hungry is like putting your thumb in your mouth. It's not bad or wrong. That attitude is just piling on the guilt. The behavior is serving an important purpose. Comfort and security are good. Instead of trying to amputate the unwanted behavior, why not find a way to meet the underlying need? Meet the need, and the client won't need a pacifier anymore.

Behaviors are learned. And Parts express through behaviors and responses. The cause of the unwanted behavior is always in the client's past. All the emotions, beliefs, and body sensations that were present when that Part formed are held by that Part. The *feeling* associated with a Part gives you the energy you need for Affect Bridge. You can Bridge back to the event that caused that Part to form, in the first place, uncover what happened to cause it to form, and identify what need it has been trying to fulfill. You can then help the client release the emotions that have been keeping her stuck in that event, emotionally. Then, find a way to satisfy the unmet need. This will free the Part to take on a newer, better, more fulfilling job.

Dialogue Work

The way to uncover the aspects calling for transformation is to have a conversation. Parts Work always involves a dialogue process. In a regression session, the conversation can just be between you and the Part. Or it can be a conversation that you facilitate between the client and a Part of themselves. For example, the Inner Child Work requires the Adult Part of the client to go back into an event from the past to have a talk with the younger Part of themselves. For the Forgiveness Work, the Adult Part is called upon to have a grownup conversation with the person who hurt them in the past.

Parts Work involves having a conversation with one or more Parts. You might be having a talk with the Child Part or a Parent Part, or it might be a nasty Part like the Perpetrator of abuse, or even something more sinister. Just remember that these are all Parts of the client. They are internal representations of either self or others that are tied to specific experiences earlier in life. This means that they are available to have a conversation provided they are willing and able to speak.

Not all Parts are able to speak. For example, I had a client who was moaning and groaning and writhing in the chair, but no matter what I tried, I couldn't get her to respond to my questions. Not only was this a real challenge to figure out what, exactly, I was dealing with, but it was also creepy! Now, you might be tempted to assume that what I was dealing with was a spiritual attachment. Believe me, it crossed my mind. But the only way you can know, for sure, is to let it be revealed to you. In this case, I called upon the Adult Part of the client to give me a report about what was happening in the scene. It turned out that the Part *could not* speak because what we were dealing with was a pre-verbal Part of the client. Never assume. Ask.

All Parts co-exist, although not always harmoniously. And when there's a conflict, the client will feel it. Restoring internal harmony will restore peace and free up the energies needed for healing.

Healing is always certain. - **A Course in Miracles**

Summary

Parts Work is a foundation for effective regression hypnotherapy. Parts make up the personality and include Child Parts, Parent Parts, Offender Parts, Malicious Parts, Body Parts, Spiritual Parts, Habitual Parts, and many more. Parts are recordings of how the person learned to cope with a specific set of circumstances.

While all Parts co-exist, they do not always do so harmoniously. All Parts are good and meant to be helpful. Many serve a protective function. But when Parts are disowned or rejected, they can become problematic. In some cases, they can take on malevolent qualities and begin acting out in self-destructive ways.

The three primary Parts we work with in regression sessions are the Inner Child, the Adult, and Offender or Parent Parts. Child Parts are feeling Parts. When there's a conflict, the client will feel it. Parent Parts are internal representations of the primary caregivers. These Parts provide the rules for being and doing. The Adult Part is the Grownup consciousness of the client in the here and now.

This Part of the client is very important to Inner Child Work because the Conscious Mind can bring mature logic and reason to the process of reviewing past events. As a result, this Part of the client has the capacity for insight and realization.

CHAPTER 15:
Inner Child Work

Inner Child Work is a process of self-change that involves taking Adult consciousness into the ISE to support the Inner Child and provide whatever was missing the first time. Primarily, this will be to provide safety, but it's also to help the Child make sense of what was happening. Bringing in Adult Consciousness allows you to Re-Story the event.

The process begins with testing to locate the Initial Sensitizing Event (ISE) as you Bridge back to earlier and earlier events. Once you have located the ISE, the next step is to uncover the internal conflict. The client becomes the Part of the client that was a Child in that event. This gives you access to thoughts and the feelings of the Child. The client is seeing through the eyes of the Child. They're hearing through the ears of the Child. They're feeling the feelings of the Child.

Peeling away the layers of thoughts and feelings will reveal the underlying Thought-Cause Alignment Pattern (TCA). Remember, the cause of the problem is the Thought. Thoughts generate emotions that drive behaviors. We follow the feeling back into the ISE because there is a direct connection between the symptom and the emotion. Behind the emotion is the Thought responsible for generating it. What's happening? How is the Child interpreting this? What meaning is being given to this experience? How is this at odds with what the Child wants?

Identify all the Thought-Emotion connections. e.g., *The Thought (not wanted) makes me feel [scared]*. What is the unmet need of the Child? Understanding the developmental needs of a child can help you to target the specific unmet need that caused the Child Part to form in the ISE.

Pre-Natal Parts

A person who is stuck in a pre-natal event may report a feeling of being incomplete, worthless, or not wanted. As an adult, they may procrastinate when it comes to starting or finishing things.

Part Formed at Birth

If a client regresses back to the birth experience, find out how the parents feel about bringing this new child into their lives. Are the parents prepared to welcome a baby into their lives? Are they joyful about the baby coming? Are they ready to take on the responsibilities of parenthood? Ambivalent parents will seed uncertainty in the Child, which generates anxiety.

Parts Formed Between Birth – 6 Months

An issue seeded between birth and six months may have issues involving the ability to trust others. They may not be fully aware of their own needs and put the needs of others first. These clients may have a pattern of numbing out. Things to explore in the birth to six-month period include: Who is the primary caregiver of the Child? Is the primary caregiver responding appropriately to the needs of the

Child? For example: Do they hold the baby and look in his eyes? Do they touch and talk to the baby lovingly? Do they sing to the child?

Parts Formed Between 6 – 18 Months

A stuck event in the period between six to eighteen months may express as problems with boredom. The client may be compulsively neat or perfectionistic. Things to explore in the six to eighteen-month period include: Is the primary caregiver consistent in their care of the Child? Is the Child safe and protected from harm? What is the conversational tone between the Parent and Child?

Parts Formed Between 18 months – 3 Years

An ISE between 18 months and 3 years may express as a preference for being right over being successful. The client may cover up fear and sadness with anger. They may bully others or act out rebelliously. They may have trouble setting boundaries or express anger indirectly. Things to explore in the 18-month to 3-year period include: Does the Child receive encouragement and praise? Does the Child receive reasonable limits? Does the Child have permission to express feelings (positive or negative)? Are the caregivers even-tempered?

Parts Formed Between 3 – 6 Years

An ISE between three and six years may find expression through a lack of assertiveness. The client may have a strong need to be in control and come out on top. They may struggle with feeling inadequate and compare themselves to others. They may have confusion regarding their identity. For example, they may define themselves by their job or a significant relationship. They may dress or behave outlandishly. Wanting or expecting magical solutions is typical of this time period. Things to explore in the three to six-year period include: Is the Child supported in exploring the world of people and things? Is it okay for the Child to explore ideas and feelings? Is the Child encouraged to express feelings? Is the Child encouraged to connected feelings and thinking? Does the Child receive answers to questions? Is the Child praised for appropriate behavior?

Set Up for Dialogue Process

While you're facilitating the uncovering work with the Child Part, the Conscious Mind or Adult Part of the client is in the role of an observer. It's just off on the sidelines. Now it's time to bring the Adult Part into the event with the Child Part. The way to do this is to give the suggestion, *Let it be as if there were two of you there now - the Grownup Part of you and the five-year-old Part of you. And just be there with the Child you once were.*

This sets up for the dialogue process you will mediate between the Child Part and the Adult Part. From now on, whenever the Adult Consciousness steps forward, the Child will take a place in the background. When the Child steps forward, the Adult will take on the observer role.

The Child has a limited capacity for interpreting situations. Things can happen that feel overwhelming to a Child that, to Adult Consciousness, can seem like no big deal. The primary role of Adult Consciousness is to step in, be a loving support to the Child, and to help the Child make sense of whatever happened in that event.

#1. Heal the SEAL

The signature of an ISE in childhood is the SEAL Pattern. Whatever happened came as a surprise. The emotional intensity felt overwhelming because the Child lacked the ability to self-regulate. But the main problem is that there was no one there to support the Child.

The Child had to deal with the situation alone.

To neutralize the SEAL Pattern, go before the event. This will be a point prior to the ISE where nothing bad has happened yet. The Child will still be feeling safe and secure. Then, bring in Adult Consciousness to prepare the Child to meet the trouble by telling him what's going to happen.

Remember, the reason there's a problem is because the client has been cut off from this Part of himself. Bringing the Adult Part into the scene *with* the Child introduces a fundamental change to the original event because the Child no longer has to face the situation alone. A grownup's job is to find a way to meet the needs of the Child. This resolves the lack. This heals the SEAL.

The goal is not to change the event. You can't. It's already happened. All you can do is create the conditions where healing can happen. Informing the Child neutralizes the initial Shock. The Child now knows what's going to happen.

The next step is to fill the Child with love. Love and fear cannot coexist. Filling the Child with love introduces contradicting energy to the original event. It may not eliminate it completely, but it will help to reduce the emotional impact when you replay the event.

#2. Find the Love

Instruct Adult Consciousness to go inside his heart and find the love. It's there. It may just be a flicker, to begin with. But what we pay attention to we get more of. Have the client find the feeling. Then, test to make sure that the client is feeling it.

The only thing that really matters is that the client is feeling the feeling. If the client cannot find the love for the Child, regress back further to where the Child is still loveable. You cannot proceed with the Inner Child Work until you have a Grownup who can love and accept the Child. Healing is about reconnecting with our Core Energy. This is the Source of all healing, including all our good feelings. Make sure that the client is feeling the love before you proceed.

#3. Feel the Love

If the client is feeling the love, amplify the feeling by bringing attention to the body. Emotions are felt in the body. What sensations are there? The client might say they're experiencing warmth in the chest or the heart. They might be experiencing a pleasant sensation flowing throughout the body. The idea is to fan the embers into a cozy fire.

If they're feeling a warm, comfortable feeling in the chest, give that feeling permission to be there. You can simply say, "That's right," or, "There's the feeling," or, "That's good. Realize that's your feeling. You're allowed to feel loved." Then, encourage the client to feel it fully. It feels good because it's flooding the body with endorphins!

Once the client is fully into the feeling, ask him to give that feeling to the Child by sending it heart to heart. This gives the Child the experience of the one thing he needs the most –to feel safe and secure, love, and acceptance. Love is the Child's natural state. Love feels good. Validate that he's allowed to feel good again. Then, instruct the client to notice how good it feels.

This is healing. Getting this kind of positive energy into the Child will change how the client feels as an adult. Guide the client to fill the Child up with his love and acceptance. Then, verify that the Child is actually receiving the love by asking, "How does the Child like that?" or "Does it seem like the Child is accepting your love?"

If the Child is accepting love from the Grownup, they'll feel it. Keep sending it in until the Child is completely filled with love. This doesn't take very long. Just give the client a moment of silence to ensure that the Child is completely filled. They'll know when it's complete because they'll feel it.

As this is happening, the energies are flowing into Adult Consciousness, as well. Remember, you are working with Parts of the same person. When the needs of the Child are met, this change will ripple outward into the client's Adult life.

When a person is feeling strong emotions, they are in a hyper-suggestible state. This is the perfect time to use auto-suggestion because you have already established a level of self-love. Invite Grownup to speak words of love and acceptance to the Child. You can help to get the ball rolling by inviting the client to say the EFT self-acceptance phrase, *I deeply and completely love and accept you.* Then, ask the client to continue speaking.

No one knows the Child better than Grownup because they are the Child, all grown up. All you need to do is suggest, "Inside of you are the words that the Child needs to hear." If the client is stuck for words, you can help by asking the client a few questions. But what the Child most needs to hear will come out of the uncovering process. For example, "Is that baby good enough? Tell him/her, 'You're good enough.' Is that baby smart enough? Tell him/her, 'You're smart enough.' Does s/he matter to you? Tell him, 'You matter to me. Your feelings brought me back to you. I'm so glad that I found you. And now that I've found you, I'm here for you. You'll never be alone."

You can't make this stuff up! Everything you need is within the Mind of the client. The uncovering procedure will give you all the details needed to achieve a lasting result.

#4. Love Heals

Inner Child Work occurs in tandem with the uncovering and releasing processes. Once you completed the initial uncovering, you'll have a general sense of the Story. You'll know what happened, who was involved, and what the Child was thinking and feeling during the experience. Now, it's time to change the Symptom Requiring Pattern by re-parenting the Child. This is also known as the Informed Child Technique. The Adult is going to resolve the Symptom Requiring Aspects trapped in the event by providing whatever the Child needs to get through the experience without feeling overwhelmed.

Re-Parent the Child

The process of re-parenting the Child begins with filling the Child with love and acceptance. This creates a bond between the Grownup Part and the Child Part. The Adult Part takes on the role of a loving Parent because that's what was missing from the first time. The bonding process of sending and receiving love establishes a level of trust between these two Parts of the client.

This is a game-changer because it restores the client's power of choice. From now on, Adult Consciousness gets to decide what needs to happen. You merely guide the process and support the client in creating change.

All healing is self-healing. Adult Consciousness has what the Child lacked – maturity. Grownup can evaluate the situation, identify errors in perceptions, and provide the understanding the Child needs to transform the event into a learning experience. That's the objective.

Once the Child has been filled with love, it's time to prepare the Child to move through the event. Only, this time, the Child will know that he's not alone. Grownup is with them. The Child will know that they are going to survive. Grownup is evidence of this. The Child will know that the moment anything happens, Grownup will be there for them.

Notice how we are establishing a Contract prior to the ISE? The client is making an informed decision to meet the trouble head-on. The Child knows that *this time*, they're not alone. Adult knows that they can handle it, they're a grownup! As the Child moves through the event, Adult Consciousness can be called upon to reality-check the Perceptions and Thoughts of the Child.

The job of Adult Consciousness is to challenge erroneous beliefs and provide contrasting knowledge. Is the Child interpreting what's happening accurately? Is it true? If the Thought is not true, the Grownup's job is to inform the Child of the truth about what's happening. This will release the emotion attached to the false perception.

If the Child is correctly interpreting the situation, then Grownup's job is to help the Child to deal with it. Bad things do happen to small people. But challenging situations early in life can be used to develop strength, wisdom, and resilience. Sometimes, it's enough to know that a painful experience or uncomfortable emotion won't last long.

Even the worst emotion won't last more than 90 seconds. What keeps a person stuck in a feeling is resisting the feeling. Allowing the feeling to be felt and expressed allows it to finish. Then, it's over. What the Child needs to know is that he will survive. Grownup is living proof that the Child will get through the experience.

The Child is innocent. There is nothing he could have done to deserve ill-treatment. For some reason, the people who were responsible for taking care of the Child didn't do their job. And if the Child made a mistake, it's forgivable. Nothing could ever change the truth about them —that they are loveable. Human beings are meant to learn from experience. The Child is learning valuable lessons that will empower them growing up. Help the client to discover what this might be. This is what Stephen Parkhill called *finding the good.*"

To forgive is to find the good. — **Stephen Parkhill**

Re-Story the ISE

Ronald Reagan's favorite joke was about a little boy whose parents were worried that he was too optimistic. Naturally, the parents took the overly-cheerful boy to a psychiatrist. In an attempt to dampen the boy's spirits, the psychiatrist ushered the boy into a room piled high with horse manure. The little boy was delighted! Clambering to the top of the pile, he dropped on all fours and began digging. "What are you doing?" the psychiatrist asked. "With all this manure," the little boy beamed, "here's got to be a pony in here somewhere!"

Healing is complete when the client can look back on their life story (the manure) and find the pony (the good). How did it benefit them? How did it make them stronger or wiser? What did they learn to do or not do, which would serve in the future? What value did it hold? What purpose did it serve?

The Prime Directive of the Body-Mind system is protection. When a broken bone heals, the site of the old break is left stronger than the bone next to it. When a deep flesh wound heals, it leaves a scar, an area of tougher skin. The result is the same when healing the human soul.

It takes some maturity to look back on our history and discover how it made us stronger. Joseph Campbell said that it wasn't until he was nearing 75 years of age that, looking back upon his life, he realized that some unseen hand had been guiding him all along. This reminds me of the poem, Footprints in the Sand:

"One night I dreamed I was walking along the beach with the Lord. Many scenes from my life flashed across the sky. In each scene, I noticed footprints in the sand. Sometimes there were two sets of footprints; other times, there was one only. This bothered me because I noticed that during the low periods of my life, when I was suffering from anguish, sorrow, or defeat, I could see only one set of footprints. So, I said to the Lord, "You promised me, Lord, that if I followed you, you would walk with me always. But I have noticed that during the most trying periods of my life, there has only been one set of footprints in the sand. Why, when I needed you most, have you not been there for me?" The Lord replied, "The years when you have seen only one set of footprints, my child, is when I carried you."

Looking back, we didn't know then what we know now. Our perceptions were based on the knowledge and wisdom we had then. The younger the age, the less history we had available from which to evaluate and respond to those circumstances. When healing is accomplished, hindsight is 20-20. It's possible to realize we're older and wiser for having been through those events, no matter how painful. We are now capable of seeing things from a higher perspective and discover how the past might have served a purpose.

It's been said that it's an ill wind that blows no good. While it might not have been the best of experiences, at the time, the client can acknowledge that they made it through. After all, they're still here, still breathing. Assigning a positive meaning to these experiences will help them to relinquish their need to control externals. It will also put an end to the control the past has had over their daily living because, when the client can finally bless the past, they give themselves permission to move forward with their life, no longer feeling like a victim.

Life happens. Experience teaches us how to be and do, as well as how to not-be and not-do. What did the client learn? What valuable life lesson did those experiences provide to make them a better person? What wisdom do they now possess as a result of having been through that? As they find the good in those circumstances, they find their own good. And this is the true gold; the goodness, the spark of the Divine within them.

What does not kill me makes me stronger. - **Friedrick Nietzche**

Summary

The Inner Child Work occurs primarily in the ISE and involves a dialogue process between Adult Consciousness and the Inner Child. The Grownup consciousness is called upon to provide love and support to the Inner Child while helping to find ways to supply what the Child needs. By helping the Child make sense of their experience, clarity and peace can be restored to allow healing.

The Core Parts of the personality are shaped during the formative years of childhood before the age of five or six. The signature of an ISE in childhood is the SEAL Pattern. To neutralize the SEAL Pattern, Adult Consciousness is brought in before the ISE to prepare the Child for the experience by:

1. Finding the Love
2. Feeling the Love
3. Healing the SEAL
4. Finding the Good.

Learn more in the Ready for Regression First Session System Course here: www.tribeofhealers.com/ready-for-regression-first-session-system-course

Releasing creates space. Loving and approving of yourself, creating a space of safety, trusting and deserving and accepting, will create organization in your mind, create more loving relationships in your life, attract a new job, and a new and better place to live, and even enable your body weight to normalize. — **Louse Hay**

CHAPTER 16:
The Time It Takes

A nd so, he went on to perform his duties in hell for seven years. He didn't wash, he didn't comb or cut his hair, or pare his nails, or wipe his eyes. And the seven years passed so quickly it seemed as if he hasn't been there for more than half a year.

The basis of the devil's agreement is that the client must do the work. The Contract isn't to merely mask or manage the symptoms. It's to achieve a lasting change. The focus isn't on the symptoms. Symptoms are merely evidence of a problem calling for resolution. The focus is on the feelings. By allowing uncomfortable feelings and emotions to be a part of the process, the hidden cause is allowed to be brought to conscious awareness to be released. This requires a commitment.

The client must be prepared to do the work necessary to get a complete resolution of the problem by thoroughly cleaning house. Releasing the blocks creates the conditions where healing can happen. But it can still take time. Regression hypnotherapy isn't a single-session approach. It is a client-centered approach to therapy. The time required really depends on the client's individual needs, goals, and resources.

On average, six or seven sessions is not unreasonable and provides the time needed to test the results and ensure a lasting result. But even if it took 20 sessions to achieve a lasting result, this is still truly impressive. Counseling requires, on average, six sessions just to establish a working alliance with the client. To achieve a full recovery in 50% of psychotherapy clients requires, on average, 20 sessions, while a 75% success-rate typically requires 50 weekly sessions. This is why regression to cause hypnotherapy is considered a brief therapy.

The healing process of regression hypnotherapy begins with the Set-Up Phase, where the focus is on preparing the client to do the work necessary to be successful. What follows is the Transformation Phase, which relies on the two Rs in R2CH – Regress and Release.

Regression to Cause is a process of finding the event responsible for requiring symptoms using:

- Bridging Techniques

- Uncovering Procedure

- Tests for the ISE

- Symptom Requiring Pattern Identification

- Session Mapping

Releasing is a process that can be taught during the Set-Up Phase. It can then be used during the uncovering procedure to gain access to deeper layers of perceptions, thoughts, and feelings by utilizing techniques such as:

- Find the Feeling

- Quantify the Feeling

- Stir Up the Feeling

- Follow the Feeling

#1. Find It!

1. Find the feeling for Affect Bridge
2. Bridge back to the earlier event (SSE)
3. Preliminary Uncovering Procedure
4. Test for ISE
5. Bridge back to ISE
6. Uncover Story trapped in ISE (What's happening?)
7. Identify Parts involved in Story (Who?)

#2. Feel It!

Energy trapped in the nervous system of the body is uncomfortable. It can generate resistance and block awareness. Releasing trapped emotional energy restores peace and clarity to the Mind-Body system. This will give you a more cooperative client, allowing you to continue Bridging back to the ISE. It also makes it easier to uncover the details trapped in an event.

#3. Heal It!

Releasing brings relief. As a result, the Mind becomes increasingly more receptive to new programming. This is the purpose of the Inner Child

Work. The goal of the uncovering procedure is to identify the unmet

needs of the Child. Helping the client to meet these needs will resolve the underlying need for symptoms.

Once you have identified what is at odds with what the Child wants, the Adult Consciousness of the client assumes a parental role to their younger self. The Grownup's job is to resolve the Symptom Requiring Aspects by:

- Providing loving support

- Reality checking perceptions

- Finding contrasting knowledge

- Challenging erroneous beliefs

The Transforming Phase is comprised of two steps in the seven-phase protocol:

4.   Regress & Release

5.   Inner Child Work

The final phase is the Verification Phase, where you will take measures to ensure a lasting change.

PHASE 3: VERIFY

Verification Phase	
6 Testing	7 Forgiveness Work
Test & Integrate Changes	*Effortless Permanence*
6.1 Test the ISE	7.1 Restore Goodness
6.2 Test the SSEs & Compound Changes	7.2 Release the Grievance
6.3 Test the Results in Real Life	7.3 Forgiveness Test
	7.4 Reclaim Wholeness
	7.5 Age Progression

Feelings are like a human thermometer. A thermometer tells what temperature it is, which in turn helps us decide what to wear. Feelings tell us about the temperature of our internal processes and help us decide how to be and what to do. — **Virginia Satir**

CHAPTER 17:
Test the Results

When his time was finally up, the devil comes and says, "Well, Hans, what have you done all this time?" And Hans gave him a report, "Well, I've tended the fires under the caldrons, swept up and carried the sweepings behind the door."

This is the first time in the story that the soldier is referred to as Hans! This indicates that a change has occurred! The client has come to himself in some regard. What has Hans been doing all this time? The first three Universal Healing steps!

1. Find the ISE by regressing and releasing.
2. Feel the feelings to reveal the underlying root cause.
3. Heal the Child Part that has been trapped in that event.

The fourth step is to Seal it by making sure the results are going to last. How do you know if all the contributing aspects have been let go of? How do you know if the client is truly free of the past? How can you know when your work is complete? You test. The only way to know anything, for sure, is to test the results.

"But," said the devil, "you also looked into the caldrons! Good thing you put on more wood, or you'd have lost your life."

The devil knows that every condition demands a life. The client must willingly let go of the life he has been living. Serious disease *literally* demands a life. While anger is a natural response to perceived hurts, when anger is culturally viewed as bad, only a devil would encourage a person to express it. This is precisely what is called for. Holding onto fear, anger, hurt, resentment, rage, blame, condemnation, and thoughts of punishment only hurts the client. So, the devil is saying, "Good thing you got it out!"

Taking the lid off their feelings has brought the client face to face with the toxic contents of their own Mind. That takes courage. Had Hans avoided forbidden memories or feelings, the moment of deliverance would have been lost. The problem would have slipped back into the shadows and, with it, the solution. While he might have enjoyed some short-term relief, the symptoms would eventually find a way to resurface. Or worse.

If the client is to heal fully, they must be prepared to forgive the past. Only then will past events have no further power to control them. But most people don't know what it means to forgive the past. Instead of forgiveness, they use:

- Denial: ignore and play down the experience.

- Self-blame: explain their experience in terms of their own actions or behaviors.

- Victim Identity: stay stuck in self-pity, helplessness, woundology."

- Indignation: foster anger, intolerance, revengefulness.

- Survivor Identity: distance themselves from the hurtful experience by seeing themselves as a survivor.

Total healing requires a complete release of all negative feelings. That's what it means to forgive the past. Forgiveness is a letting go. What the client is being asked to do is let go of the problem. Releasing the toxic thought and emotional energies trapped inside will empower the client to relinquish his Victim Identity. As he reclaims his authentic power, he will experience a complete cessation of symptom expression and effortless permanence.

"Well, it looks like your time is up. Do you want to go back home?"
"Oh, yes," said the soldier. "I should very much like to see what my father is doing at home."

Did you notice that *the soldier* responded to the question, not Hans? What this tells us is that Hans is still holding onto his tough little soldier stance. There's a Part of him that's still stuck in survival mode. This is also the first mention of dear old Dad! Clearly, something is not resolved.

In the movie *Shrek,* there's a conversation between the ogre, Shrek, and his friend, Donkey, where Shrek asserts, "There's more to ogres than people think."

Shrek: *Ogres are like onions! (Holds up an onion, which Donkey sniffs.)*

Donkey: *They stink?*

Shrek: Yes . . . No!

Donkey: Oh, they make you cry?

Shrek: No!

Donkey: Oh, you leave them out in the sun, they get all brown, start sprouting little white hairs.

Shrek: (Peels an onion.) NO! L-A-Y-E-R-S. Onions have layers. Ogres have layers. Onions have layers. You get it? We both have layers. (Walks off.)

Donkey: Oh, you both have L-A-Y-E-R-S. Oh. You know, not everybody likes onions. What about cake? Everybody loves cake!

Shrek: I don't care what everyone else likes! Ogres are not like cakes.

Donkey: You know what else everybody likes? Parfaits! Have you ever met a person, and you say, "Let's get some parfait," they say, "Hell no, I don't like no parfait"? Parfaits are delicious!

Shrek: NO! You dense, irritating, miniature beast of burden! Ogres are like onions!

The devil knows that, like onions and ogres, memories have layers. You need to work through the many layers to identify all the contributing aspects. The problem is that you're always working against the clock; there's only so much you can do in a single session.

No matter how thorough you might be in addressing all the contributing aspects, there is no guarantee that you have found all the roots of the client's problem. Deeper layers of truth can be withheld until the Subconscious Mind feels that it's safe to reveal them. So, you won't necessarily uncover the whole Story right away.

The client can consciously choose to withhold some piece of information because they judge it unimportant or too shameful to admit to. But if it's not brought to light, you can't fix it. Whatever the client fails to disclose is still there, calling for release. Left unresolved, the problem will persist. This is why you must test the results.

#1. Test the ISE

To test the results in the ISE, the client reviews the event from start to finish. The event plays out exactly as it did the first time. The only thing that changes is how the client feels. Healing is not about changing history. Healing is about changing how the client feels on the *inside* in such a way that they are no longer bound to the things of the past.

The past is just the past. The future lies in their ability to learn from past experiences and be so transformed by them so that situations and people in daily life no longer negatively affect them. The ISE doesn't change. What changes is how it feels. When the client can move through the event without getting triggered, the event has been cleared.

Gather Up Insights

"You've earned your reward,' said the Devil. "Here's how to get it: go behind the door and fill your knapsack with sweepings, and take them home with you."

When the client can calmly accept what happened, free of the perceptions and judgments that initially caused them distress, a new level of order and stability is established. The moment the client recognizes this change, it becomes permanent.

To encourage this new level of awareness, ask the client, "What's changed?" This question is an insight-generator. Let the client tell you what specific changes are now being realized. This allows the event to become a learning experience, transforming how the client sees themselves and the world around them. As a result, they will respond to similar situations in the future very differently. This is setting up for the process of progressing through the SSEs.

To realize is to make real. What is the client discovering? What has changed? Is it true? How do they know it's true? All evidence to support change should come out of the client's experience during the session. Don't use a script. Reinforce the client's own realizations. The more meaning the client can find in their Story, the added inner resources they will gather, and the more profound the transformation will be.

You can deepen the transformation by suggesting, *You've changed!* Then ask, "How do you know you've changed?" Validate the client's recognition of change. Then, ask, "How does knowing this change things from now on?" This will tell you what the client expects in the future. You are installing new beliefs, so make sure to connect these changes to the client's Therapeutic Goal.

What the Mind expects tends to be realized. - **Gerald Kein**

The ISE is an experience where a Part of the client got stuck in childhood. As a result, it has been unable to grow up. Releasing trapped emotions will create a state of high suggestibility. Inner Child Work takes advantage of this state by installing concepts and ideas that are aligned with the Child's Core State of health and happiness.

The next step is to transfer these changes to Adult Consciousness by helping the Child to grow up. The way to do this is to instruct the Child to gather up all the changes – the insights and better feelings – and take ownership of them. Encourage the Child to embody these changes by feeling them fully. Then, grow the Child up by progressing through the SSEs.

#2. Test the SSEs

Growing the Child up is a process of Future Pacing from the ISE through the SSEs on the client's Storyline. This allows you to test the results that occurred in the ISE, compound all changes, and transform the client's Storyline. This is where your Session Map is going to really help you because it gives you a visual map of the client's Storyline.

Each SSE represents a *future* event to the Child that has been trapped in the ISE. By progressing through the SSEs, the Child is set free of that event and is allowed to grow up into adulthood, knowing what they know now. As a result, Adult Consciousness receives all the benefits of change.

The specific changes that have been realized are now going to go with the Child as he grows up to the next SSE on the timeline. So, once the ISE is clear, instruct the Child to gather up the newer, better state of awareness and bring these changes with them to the next significant event. For example, if the ISE was at age two, and the next SSE on the timeline is at age five, the Child is instructed to *grow up* to that situation at age five with the memory of everything they learned in the ISE. The SSE is then reviewed by the transformed Child.

This is how you get a lasting result. Clear everything that is connected to the client's presenting issue in the ISE. Then, install the resources that the Inner Child didn't have the first time. This means that the Child moving forward in life is not the same person anymore. They've changed! Because they've changed, the SSEs will change to reflect how events *would* have played out had the Child not been so reactive.

But, if the Child gets triggered by something in an SSE, check to see if that aspect existed in the ISE. If it was a problem in the ISE, the ISE is not clear yet. Go back to the causal event, find the feeling, and conduct the Feeling Test. There could be an earlier event connected to that feeling. Complex issues can have multiple ISEs feeding into the same symptoms. The feeling may lead back to the same ISE, or you may discover that there is another ISE. Either way, you'll know what to focus on next.

If the aspect that is brought to light wasn't in the ISE, then it's probably something that got added to the overall pattern *after* the ISE. In this case, release it in the SSE. Then, rewind and replay the event again. Test to make sure the SSE is clear. Then, before moving onto the next SSE, grab the opportunity to compound change by asking the Child, "What's changed?" Let the client tell you. Then, validate the client's insights with, "YOU have changed!"

Teach the client to take ownership of every positive change that has occurred. In this way, you can heal the Storyline as the Child is growing up. This utilizes the Subconscious Mind's natural tendency to generalize all learning.

Generalize Change

All these changes are rippling forward along the timeline, all the way up to the client in the here and now. As you support the Child in growing in wisdom and understanding, you are growing and empowering Adult Consciousness.

As the client moves forward along the timeline, the changes will ripple outward into other experiences or events that may or may not have been brought to light during the regression. Other Parts of the client can derive benefit from these changes. As a result, issues that are seemingly unrelated to the client's presenting issue will often resolve on their own, as if by magic.

Integrate Change

Grow the Child up to the client sitting in the chair. Then, anchor the changes in the here and now by guiding the client to notice how much better they *do* feel. Acknowledge and celebrate success by encouraging the client to claim responsibility for having created these wonderful changes. Tell the client, "You did that!" Then, give the Subconscious Mind instructions to integrate all changes – physically, mentally, emotionally, spiritually – allowing every Part of the client to benefit from these wonderful changes. Know that the process of embodying real and lasting change has been initiated.

#3. Test the Results in Real Life

"Oh, and you must also go unwashed and uncombed, with long hair and a long beard, with uncut nails and bleary eyes. And if anyone asks you where you've come from you must say, 'From hell.' And if they ask you who you are, you must say, 'The devil's grimy brother and my king as well!'"

In ancient times, the king was solely responsible for his own kingdom (reality) and answerable to no one but God (higher Power). To be your *own king* is to be sovereign. Autonomy is true power. Self-rule is the ability to respond to external conditions with authority.

The client is committed to a process of reclaiming authority over their life. The devil is merely reminding him of the Contract. The Contract is an agreement to allow uncomfortable feelings to be a part of the healing process. So, the devil says, "Oh, by the way, you're going to be more aware of your feelings because of the good work you've done today."

The devil is also reminding the client of the Therapeutic Relationship. "We're in this together (brothers). We stick with it until we get the healing. If anything comes up between sessions, you let me know." This ensures that, should the client get triggered or experiences a recurrence of symptoms, they won't bail on the process. They'll know to come back and give you a full report. This is keeping the Contract open.

Keep the Contract Open

Healing is a process, not an event. Cleaning house in the ISE and growing the Child up through the SSEs begins the process of healing at a Subconscious level of Mind. But you can only resolve what is brought to light during the session. The Subconscious Mind is only going to show you what it feels the client is ready for. And change doesn't happen in the session. It happens in the client's waking life. That's where post-hypnotic suggestions take effect. The only way to know, for sure, that the problem has been completely resolved is to test the client's responses in everyday life.

Think of the time between sessions as a *soaking in* period where suggestions for change will either take effect or be challenged. If nothing changes, nothing changes. So, something should happen between sessions. The client may feel better, worse, or experience some ups and downs. This provides the information you need to guide the healing process effectively. So long as something is happening between sessions, progress is being made and tells you what needs to happen next.

If the client comes back and reports that they felt better, this tells you the client was able to hold onto the changes. Progress has been made. That's something worth celebrating!

If the client experiences some ups and down between sessions, there's movement indicating that change is occurring. Nothing breeds success like success! So, validate every sign of success before moving onto the next piece of the puzzle.

Even when the client leaves your office feeling great, they may not be able to hold onto the better feelings. Two or three days later, they may do a deep dive back into the muck. If the client feels worse or gets triggered, it simply that you haven't resolved the whole problem yet.

Taking the lid off past events naturally stirs things up at a Subconscious level of Mind. As a result, it's going to be working behind the scenes, recalibrating to all the shifts that have occurred. It's going to be integrating these changes as part of the client's life, NOW. But Love brings up everything, unlike itself, to be healed.

When you poke a hole in a pocket of venom, it releases some of the internal pressure. And when the Subconscious Mind gets some relief, it is going to want more relief. As a result, it will start pushing more stuff up to the surface so it can be resolved. Dreams can reflect this process, and memories can bubble up to the surface of awareness, unexpectedly. This is great news because the next layer is being made accessible for healing.

Some people have to go back into situations that are difficult. They still have to deal with situational stress at home or in the workplace. There might be a problem in the family system or primary relationship about which you know nothing. When an issue is not completely resolved, old responses can get triggered by situations and people's daily lives.

Whatever the status quo is in the client's life is a support system for the problem. Creating inner change will upset that status quo. As a result, children may start acting out. Spouses may become argumentative. Bosses or co-workers may challenge the client's ability to hold onto positive changes. Like it or not, their opinions matter to the client. But the client's healing cannot be dependent on the opinions or behavior of others. If something happens to trigger the client, this gives you a specific event you can use to bring up a Bridge to the causal event.

These people cannot be expected to think or behave any differently than they have in the past. After all, they haven't changed – the client changed. But the people closest to them have the power to sabotage the client's progress by unconsciously attempting to reinstall the old, familiar programming. Keeping the Contract open provides a lifeline so that, should something happen to trigger the client in daily life, they won't give up on themself. The client will remember that they are engaged in a process that will set them free of the past by reclaiming their right to feel their truest feelings.

Time will tell. So, instruct the client to carry these changes with them into their everyday life to test the results. Remind them that when everything has been cleared, they will no longer be susceptible to people and situations as in the past. When things happen in the present life, which serves as reminders of past experiences, they will no longer have any power to affect how the client feels. This is true emotional freedom.

I am the master of my fate. I am the captain of my soul. - **Henley**

Time Will Tell

The soldier held his peace and did as the devil had instructed without complaint, but he wasn't at all pleased with his reward.

During a week-long training in Florida, I had the honor of experiencing a Regression to Cause hypnotherapy session with Stephen Parkhill. It was not at all what I expected! There was no relaxation. Instead, I was taken on a breath-taking, roller-coaster ride into an early childhood event. Clearing the many layers of emotions in the ISE restored clarity and peace. And yet, immediately following the session, I felt disoriented and a little down. Perhaps, I was still processing. But I didn't mention this to anyone. I also didn't mention that I wasn't pleased with the lack of visual images. I had expected regression to be a 3D experience. Instead, it was more dreamlike, as if I were seeing things through heavy gauze.

While the emotions were visceral and real, I couldn't help but wonder if I hadn't just made it all up. This taught me an important lesson. Clients don't tell you everything. Some clients continue to hope for a single-session miracle, despite being educated to the contrary. Others may think that once healed, they can resume a toxic relationship or a lifestyle responsible for the symptoms. That's an unrealistic expectation. You can't override the law of Cause and Effect. Nobody can. All you can do is work with Nature.

If the client expects you to wave your magic wand, they won't be pleased with their rewards. For example,

Client: After I lose the weight, if I go back to eating normally, will I gain the weight back again?

Devil: By eating *normally*, do you mean doing what made you fat, to begin with?

Shameful truths can be brought to light during a regression session, which the client may choose not to share with you. Some clients will have niggling doubts about the process, wondering if those memories were real or imagined. Others may be unhappy about being asked to face painful memories from the past. Even when releasing uncomfortable feelings brings relief, the client can be annoyed with you for asking them to *go there*. They may be displeased to discover that real change requires real effort or that healing takes time.

All you can do is guide the process. The client is responsible for the results. All healing is self-healing. It takes effort. It depends on the client's participation. And the time it takes isn't up to you. It's up to the client. If the client chooses to withhold information that might be critical to their healing, there's nothing you can do. If they're not willing to hold up their end of the Contract, you can't make them. All you can do is work with what you're given and test the results.

Healing happens. Time will tell when the issue has been resolved for good.

To be successful, develop the persistence and doggedness and the willingness to work hard for twenty-two minutes to make sense of something that most people would give up on after thirty seconds. -
Malcolm Gladwell

Side Benefits

As soon as he was back in the woods again, he took his knapsack off his back to empty it. He was actually going to throw the sweepings away, but when he opened the pack, he discovered the sweepings have turned to pure gold. "Wow! This is a pleasant surprise," he said to himself and was well-pleased.

Because the Mind works through association, the feelings being released during a regression session can be connected to *other* situations, thoughts, feelings, and behaviors. As a result, the client may be pleasantly surprised to discover seemingly unrelated problems being resolved, even before the presenting issue has been resolved.

Some of the unexpected side-benefits reported by actual clients include:

- An anxiety sufferer is amazed to find that her craving for chocolate has disappeared completely.
- A blocked artist starts having creative and inspiring dreams.
- A stressed-out businesswoman is delighted to effortlessly reduce two pant sizes.
- A weight-loss client's psychiatrist says, "What have you been doing? Your depression is lifting!"

While I left my regression session with Parkhill questioning my experience, I needed to check things out in my waking life. I had no conscious recall of any of the events I had visited. The earliest experience was just prior to and including my birth. When I got home, I shared what I had experienced with my Mom. I was pleasantly surprised when she corroborated the events I had revisited.

A week later, I was well-pleased to discover the breast lump, which had been my presenting issue, was completely gone. Subsequent medical tests came up clean. This stuff works, folks! Never doubt it. Just test the results in the client's daily life because healing happens. The question is: Can the client hold onto the results in real life?

Summary

No matter how thorough you might be in addressing all the contributing aspects, there is no guarantee that you have found *all* the roots of the client's problem. Deeper layers of truth can be withheld until the Conscious or Subconscious Mind feels safe in revealing them. So, you must test.

The process of testing begins in the Initial Sensitizing Event. Reviewing the event allows you to test to ensure that it's clear. You can then gather all the insights and benefits of change and project them forward along the client's timeline. As these changes are carried forward, the Child bets to experience what it's like to have this newer, better level of consciousness. As they move through Subsequent Sensitizing Events, you can test for unresolved or residual aspects and clear them.

The Subconscious Mind naturally generalizes all change, so as this process is occurring, there is a ripple effect outward into other events that may not have been brought to awareness. Other Parts of the client can benefit from these changes, as well. This can result in many unexpected side-benefits of the healing process.

As these changes ripple up into the Adult Consciousness of the client, they are integrated as a component of the client's identity NOW. Future Pacing can be used to test the client's expectations for the future. The final test of the results is in the client's daily life. Can the client hold onto the changes? Time will tell. Until then, keep the Contract open.

i.   Abraham Maslow, *Hierarchy of Needs.*
ii.   Thorwald Dethlefsen, *The Healing Power of Illness* (1983).
iii.   Caroline Myss, *Why People Don't Heal* (1998).
iv.   You'll find some useful concepts regarding self-responsibility in Gary John Bishop's book, Unfuck Yourself.
v.   Dave Elman, *Hypnotherapy* (1964).
vi.   Alexander Loyd, *The Healing Code* (2013). This book provides a wealth of information on how stress is the underlying contributor to virtually every issue, giving you a great resource for educating yourself and others about the causes of dis-ease and how healing can happen.
vii.   emofree.com
viii.   eftdownunder.com
ix.   Gary Craig, *EFT for PTSD* (2009).
x.   Konrad Stettbacher, *Making Sense of Suffering* (1930).
xi.   Konrad Stettbacher, *Making Sense of Suffering* (1930).
xii.   Robert Johnson, *The Fisher King* (1993).
xiii.   When there are multiple events of a repetitive nature (e.g. ongoing abuse by the same offender) it is possible to consolidate *every* time into a single event and process them as if they were a single event.
xiv.   Mary Stevenson, *Footprints* (1936).
xv.   Michael Lambert, *Bergin and Garfield's Handbook of Psychotherapy and Behavior Change* (2013).
xvi.   Dr. Sidney B. Simon and Suzanne Simon, Forgiveness: *How to make peace with your past and get on with your life* (1991). Luskin, F., Forgive for Good (2002).

xvii. *Shrek*, directed by Andrew Adamson and Vicky Jenson (2001; USA: DreamWorks).

xviii. Sondra Ray, *Loving Relationships* (1995).

xix. Matt Sison.

CHAPTER 18:
The Only True Test

H e then proceeded to the nearest town, where an innkeeper was standing in the doorway of his inn. When the innkeeper saw Hans coming along, he was frightened to death because Hans looked awful, worse than a scarecrow. "Where have you come from?" he asked. "From hell," replied Hans. "Who are you?" asked the innkeeper. "The devil's grimy brother, and my own king as well," replied Hans.

Just as situations in daily life can act as reminders of experiences from the past, people in everyday life can trigger unresolved issues. What the client has just come face to face with is a projection of their Inner Critic. Projection is a term used in psychology to describe the process of avoiding uncomfortable feelings or impulses by attributing them to someone else. For example, a bully might deny his own feelings of vulnerability by projecting them onto his victims.

Recall how Hans wanted to see how his father was doing. Similar to a father, an innkeeper's job is to provide for basic human needs — lodging, food, and drink. This is someone whom the client is dependent upon, in some way. It might be a parent or someone who plays a surrogate-parent role such as a spouse, employer, doctor, member of the clergy, etc. who has the power to withhold, block or deny important needs fulfillment.

Needs Fulfillment

Maslow's Hierarchy of Needs illustrates the needs, values, drives, and priorities which dominate human motivation and behavior. The base of the pyramid represents *physical needs*, which are basic to human survival – oxygen, water, food, clothing, shelter, sex, etc.

When physical needs are met, the *need for safety* takes precedence and will drive behavior. Safety needs express as a desire for predictability, order, and fairness. These include personal security, financial security, health and well-being, and protection against potential threats such as accident or illness, e.g., car's safety features, job security, savings account, insurance policies, pension fund, etc.

After physical and safety needs are fulfilled, emotional and *social needs* take precedence. This includes the need for love and belonging. When the need to love and be loved is unmet, loneliness, social anxiety, and clinical depression may manifest. This need for belonging can often overcome the physiological and security needs, depending on the strength of the peer pressure; an anorexic, for example, may ignore the need to eat and the security of health for a feeling of control and belonging.

Above the need for love and belonging is the *need for self-esteem/self-respect*. The lower form expresses as a need to be accepted and valued by others; status, recognition, fame, prestige, and attention. The higher form rests on inner competence gained through experience resulting in a sense of strength and empowerment, mastery, self-confidence, and independence.

While the lower four layers of the pyramid represent *deficiency needs*, the pinnacle of the pyramid is *self-actualization*. This represents the desire to become more oneself and realize one's full potential. Interestingly, the army's recruiting song for the past 20 years has been, "Be all that you can be!" This is psychological *kingship*. To achieve this level of self-knowledge, one must first satisfy each previous level of need –physical, safety, love, and self- esteem.

To reclaim their right to self-rule, the client's self-worth cannot be dependent on the opinion of others. For example, the weight-loss client stops punishing herself for being overweight and begins finding ways to enjoy life *while* losing the weight. Instead of waiting until she loses all the weight, she gradually gets rid of her fat clothes, replacing them with new outfits that look and feel good. She accepts invitations out with friends. She gets a massage. She books a long-overdue vacation. Even though she hasn't yet achieved her goal weight yet, she's finding ways to meet her *most important need*, which is to feel good about herself. As a result, the weight is slipping off.

When Edwin C. Barnes climbed down from the freight train in Orange, NJ, more than 50 years ago, he may have resembled a tramp, but his thoughts were those of a king! - **Napoleon Hill**

Triggered

The innkeeper didn't want to let him enter, but when Hans showed him his gold, the innkeeper unlatched the door himself.

Hans ordered the best room and the finest service and proceeded to eat and drink his fill. He adhered to the devil's instructions and didn't wash or comb his hair. And finally, he lay down to sleep.

The client adheres to the Contract. They remember that they're involved in a process of self-change to reclaim authority over his own life. The client is not focusing on the symptoms. They're focusing on finding ways to satisfy their needs by honoring their truest feelings. But remember, the soldier's problem was *not enough*. Their presenting issue was one of worthless-ness. The question is, can the client remain conscious when faced with someone who judges them as inadequate, unsuccessful, and less-than?

Feeling secure isn't the same as feeling loved. When faced with the threat of rejection, Hans tries to pacify the innkeeper by showing him the gold. The moment this happens, the client hands over power and authority (kingship) to the one person who has the power to rob them of their peace, self-worth, confidence, and happiness. They've been triggered!

Hans is vulnerable to the innkeeper because he's still *grimy*. He has reclaimed some autonomy, but when he hides his truest feelings, there's only one place left to go. Asleep. That's depression. Alice Miller wrote, "Autonomy that is not genuine ends in depression."

The innkeeper is the Saboteur who comes in many guises. He could be the co-workers who bring cakes, cookies, and chocolate goodies to work when the client boasts of her newfound freedom from chocolate. He could be a colleague who points out flaws when the artist shows his latest work-in-progress. He could be the doctor who refuses treatment unless the patient submits solely to chemical or surgical interventions. He could be the spouse who starts cooking his favorite, fattening foods when the weight loss client starts to look fit and slim.

Returning a client into a toxic family system before they're healed means running the risk of having the problem re-seeded. The client may get triggered and react unconsciously. They may experience a relapse or recurrence of symptoms. When this happens, there's always a reason. In this case, the reason is often a who.

The Key to Healing

All this time, the innkeeper hadn't been able to get that full bag of gold out of his mind. The thought of it gave him no peace. So finally, late that night, he crept in and stole it.

This part of the fairy tale reminds me of the story in Genesis about Jacob, who, in his youth, uses deceit to steal his twin brother's birthright. He then goes out into the world to achieve everything he wants in life – wife, family, money, success, position. It takes 20 years but, eventually, his past catches up with him when his brother rolls into town. The thought of having to face his brother fills Jacob with fear. He fears for his life. He fears that he will lose his family, his wealth, his position. The thought of it gives him no peace. Then, in his sleep, he is visited by a dark angel. Jacob wrestles with this angel all night long. Even though he injures his hip, he refuses to let go until the angel gives him a blessing.

This is the key to healing. The blessing lies in the symptoms themselves. Remember, symptoms are not the problem. Symptoms are Subconscious communication pointing to an unresolved issue from the past. When triggered in waking life, the Subconscious Mind will go to work on the unresolved issue. This can stir up disturbing dreams.

The Subconscious Mind does not make a distinction between real and imagined. As far as the Subconscious Mind is concerned, a dream is an actual event.

Dreams are the natural domain of the Subconscious Mind. They can show you exactly what the Subconscious Mind is working on, what it feels is important. This is why it's always wise to sleep on it before making an important decision. Dreams show us what the Conscious Mind doesn't know, can't fix, or is trying to avoid seeing. They reveal unfulfilled wishes and unmet needs. The problem is that, like symptoms, dreams can be uncomfortable. Often, they're cryptic. This is because the Subconscious Mind doesn't speak the same language as the Conscious Mind. It does not use the language of adult reasoning and logic. It uses the language of the Child – imagination, and emotion.

Over time, the Subconscious Mind develops a symbolic language that is unique to the individual, based on personal experiences, growing up. This is why the only person who can interpret your dreams is you. It's also why all healing is self-healing. It's your Mind! If a client reports that they had a disturbing dream between sessions, treat it as you would any triggering event. Invite the client to share their dream with you. Make sure the client uses present-tense language. That way, as they tell the Story, the client will be reliving the dream with you. The moment the client bumps into a feeling, you have a bridge to the actual event responsible for creating that feeling. Focus on that feeling!

Symptom Recurrence

When Hans got up the next morning and prepared to pay the innkeeper so he could leave, he realized his knapsack was gone. He thought to himself: 'I'm in trouble through no fault of my own,' and straightway decided what to do.

Whether through a triggering event or a dream, the innkeeper provokes a recurrence of symptoms. Maybe the sense of peace, self-worth, and self-acceptance that the client enjoyed immediately following the session has evaporated. Perhaps they are feeling anxious or irritated. Maybe they feel empty or depressed. This is the fundamental purpose of keeping the Contract open. The Contract is a lifeline forged by the commitment to realize a complete resolution of the problem. You won't know who or what is calling for resolution until you test the results in the client's waking life.

Keeping the Contract open ensures that the client won't blame themself. They won't decide hypnosis doesn't work. The client recognizes that there's something still calling for resolution. It's not their fault. It's just how the Mind works. Taking responsibility for your life does not mean looking to find fault or blame. It means recognizing when you have been triggered and making a conscious decision to do something about it. The problem is that the client is still looking to place blame. Any grievance is like a small ember that will eventually be fanned into a flame with time. The client cannot know true freedom so long as their well-being is contingent upon externals such as approval, performance, behavior, etc. True power comes from within.

Darlene

Three years prior to seeing me, Darlene had been in a motor vehicle accident. The rear-ender resulted in neck and leg problems that prevented her from exercising. Two years later, she was rear-ended again, this time preventing her from working. Her job loss, which provided a sense of accomplishment and financial autonomy, surfaced deep feelings of worthlessness. After ongoing physiotherapy and substantial weight gain, she had spiraled down into depression and didn't know where to turn. That's when she decides to try hypnotherapy.

During the intake process, Darlene referred to herself as "the disgrace of the family." Her mother was described as critical and disapproving, and her siblings, following Mom's modeling, treated her with disrespect. Feeling attacked, she had alienated herself from her family and was no longer speaking to Mom.

While Darlene had a whole laundry list of issues, including weight gain, physical pain, lack of sleep, lack of motivation, and beating herself up over not being a good wife and mother, her primary goal was to "get herself back." She believed that reclaiming her self-worth and self-confidence would give her the motivation she needed to accomplish the things she wanted (e.g., get a job), stop personalizing things said or done by family members, and stick up for herself when criticized by her spouse.

The fourth of nine children, Darlene's mom always had a baby. Love applied to babies up to the age of three. This was the age Darlene was when Mom's first-born daughter died. In her grief, Mom became disconnected and distant from Darlene.

At age 11, the family moved from Europe to Canada. As a result, Darlene missed classes in sexual education, a subject that Mom avoided. This left Darlene unprepared for encounters with the opposite sex in her teens. Pregnancy at age 15 added shame to her sexual confusion. Being forced to give up her baby brought deep feelings of loss reminiscent of her own childhood. A mere three years after giving up her child for adoption, Darlene's closest and dearest sibling was killed by a hit-and-run driver.

Marriage in her 20's and two children brought great joy. Marital bliss, however, came to a grinding halt when the love of her life was caught having an affair. An ugly divorce followed and, with it, more grief. She eventually remarried her present husband of 20 years.

After their first pregnancy ended with a miscarriage, Darlene was unable to lose weight. Another pregnancy gave her another daughter, who became the apple of her father's eye. The children he had adopted from her first marriage, however, were not so well-received.

The husband, a social drinker, frequently drank to excess. He also smoked marijuana at social gatherings and sometimes at home in the shed. Darlene abstained from substances to responsibly fulfill her role as a designated driver, a duty she deeply resented. Not being able to work because of the accidents made her financially dependent upon a spouse who maintained a tight fist on the money.

The innkeeper in Darlene's life was her husband.

When a client begins to change, the spouse's behavior may get better, or worse, or become erratic in response to the client's changed demeanor. In Darlene's case, spending money on hypnosis gave him no peace. He routinely challenged her decisions with attempts to make her feel guilty (worse than a scarecrow). In defense of her actions, Darlene showed him how much she was benefiting from her sessions. She was no longer depressed. She was planning meals, walking daily, and had already lost pounds and inches.

Her husband, however, became increasingly critical, pointing out shortcomings at every opportunity. Bound and determined to restore the status quo, he started drinking more frequently. He made promises which he then reneged. He even set up a *boy's room* where he and his drinking/pot-smoking buddies could congregate. Each time he succeeded in triggering Darlene emotionally, he stole her gold. Darlene would lose her peace and become defensive or aggressively pick fights in an attempt to get *him* to change.

Fortunately, Darlene stuck to her guns long enough to resolve her depression. Feeling better about herself empowered her to secure a good-paying job. She reclaimed her financial freedom by opening a bank account in her own name and began up the corporate ladder to become a trainer.

Darlene now feels good about herself and her accomplishments. Her relationships with parents and siblings have improved; she is no longer the outsider. Her ex-husband has come back into her life, and, for the first time, he has a relationship with his children. Darlene is now able to speak up for herself, express how she feels, and ask for what she wants. She has found her enthusiasm and pursues spiritual studies, despite her innkeeper-husband's disapproval. He refuses to spend money on travel, so she takes trips without him to go on spiritual pilgrimages or visit family in Europe.

While Darlene has gotten herself back, in many regards, she still hadn't faced the innkeeper in her life. She had contemplated divorce but chose to remain married to an emotionally unexpressive alcoholic. She admits that, while she loves her husband, he is unwilling and unlikely to change. As a result, life for Darlene remained stuck on an emotional roller coaster, struggling to get her husband to change so that she can be happy.

The Offender

Any vulnerability to triggering indicates that there is something still unresolved. When the button-pusher is Someone, the key to freedom lies in forgiveness.

7 Reasons to Forgive

Recent studies reveal the following:

1. People who are forgiving report fewer health problems.
2. Forgiveness leads to less stress.
3. Forgiveness leads to fewer physical symptoms of stress.
4. Failure to forgive can contribute to heart disease.
5. People who imagine not forgiving someone show negative changes in blood pressure, muscle tension, and immune response.
6. People who imagine forgiving their offender note an immediate improvement in their cardiovascular, muscular, and nervous system.
7. People who blame other people for their troubles and not forgive them have higher incidences of illnesses such as cardiovascular disease and cancer.

The Offender is the person being held responsible for the client's pain. But when the Offender is still in the client's present life, the challenge is to extinguish any power *future* trespasses that person might hold over her. As long as Darlene demands that husband change – stop drinking, be romantic, express his feelings, show that he cares – she's saying,

"I'm in trouble through no fault of my own." In other words, "It's his fault!" This is projection.

Projection is a psychological coping strategy that attempts to avoid uncomfortable feelings associated with guilt and shame by shifting the blame onto someone else. The problem is that it doesn't get rid of the problem. Blame and resentment won't change the people around us. And trying to throw away feelings of hurt, sorrow, fear, anger, or condemnation only makes the feelings stronger, keeping the client stuck in the pain of the past.

When a person has their buttons pushed, they regress. The Child Part becomes executive, forcing Adult Consciousness to go off-line. This happened the moment Hans showed his gold to the innkeeper. He perceived that he was being judged. He felt small and vulnerable, like a child, and immediately reacted by trying to please.

To please means *to cause to feel happy and satisfied*. The term happy has evolved to be associated with good luck, success, or being greatly pleased and content. Interestingly, this is the same meaning as the word placebo.

Placebo is Latin for, "I shall please." This is exactly what we did as children. We decided to please our parents because we were dependent on them for our survival. We needed them to love and accept us so that they would take care of us. We wanted them to see us and approve of us. The problem is that Mom and Dad didn't want us; they wanted a *good boy or a good girl*. So, to please them, we cut away Parts of ourselves. As a result, we lost our connection to the source of happiness and wellbeing, our Core State of Being.

The Offender holds power over the client because, consciously or unconsciously, they are perceived as a threat. When Hans gets triggered, he regresses and responds as a child would, by pleasing. While this allows him to get his needs met, it comes at a cost. Hans soon slips into unconsciously allowing an external influence to rob him of the results.

Summary

The only way to know for certain that the client's issue has been completely resolved is to test the results in their daily life. Situations in daily life can act as reminders of experiences from the past, resulting in a recurrence of symptoms. People in everyday life can serve as projections of unresolved relationships from the past.

The client's everyday life is a petri dish for the presenting issue – that's what is familiar. Any vulnerability to triggering indicates that there is something still unresolved. When the button-pusher is Someone, the key to freedom lies in forgiveness.

i.   Abraham Maslow, *Motivation and Personality* (1954).
ii.   Wikipedia, *Maslow's Hierarchy of Needs*.
iii.   Based on the needs and drives of an individualistic nation (i.e. United States) which tends to focus more on improvement of the self; in collectivist societies, the needs of acceptance and community will outweigh the needs for freedom and individuality.
iv.   Dr. Sidney B. Simon and Suzanne Simon, Forgiveness: *How to make peace with your past and get on with your life* (1991). Luskin, F., *Forgive for Good* (2002).

I think it's about forgiveness, forgiveness. Even if, even if, you don't love me anymore. – **Heart of the Matter by Don Henley**

CHAPTER 19:
Forgiveness Work

He retraced his steps, going straight back to hell, where he told the devil his tale of woe and asked for help. The devil said, "Sit down. I'll wash you. I'll comb and cut your hair. I'll trim your nails and wipe your eyes." When the devil was finished, he gave Hans back his backpack full of sweepings.

Symptoms are Subconscious communication. If something happens between sessions to trigger a recurrence of symptoms, the client returns to the four Universal Healing Steps.

#1. Find It – Tell the Story

Telling the tale of woe about a recent triggering event will cause the feelings and emotions associated with that experience to bubble up to conscious awareness. The feeling will provide a Bridge to the causal event. Follow the feeling back until you find the ISE. Release the emotional charge holding the energy in place. Validate this change for the better. Then, change the decisions formed during that experience.

It takes consciousness to heal consciousness. If something happened in the past, we cannot change that. Nor should we try. Denial just keeps a lid on the pain of the past, keeping it alive. Facing the truth, and accepting how it was for the Child, allows the past to finally be the past, which, in turn, sets the client free to create a better future.

#2. Feel It – Wash Clean

The client cannot know their truest feelings until they accept their Inner Child, completely. The Child must be washed clean of all blame. Forgiveness Work always begins with the Child because the Child is blameless. There is nothing a child could ever do to deserve condemnation. So, the devil washes away the grime of self-blame and condemnation—for example, bad, ugly, stupid, unlovable, lazy, undeserving, not-enough, etc.

The Child is restored to his natural state of innocence through direct suggestion. For example, "There's nothing wrong with you. You've done nothing wrong. You're good. You're smart. You're allowed to learn and grow from this experience. Offender has the problem; you're not the problem. You're the Child, here. You're allowed to be a Child, knowing only goodness and love." This sets the tone for how the Child is to be treated by the client – gently, lovingly, tenderly, like an attuned mother.

#3. Heal It – Comb, Cut, Trim & Wipe

The devil then combs through the thoughts of the Child to bring to consciousness any erroneous perceptions and thoughts. That's the underlying cause. While the feelings may be based on misperceptions, they are always congruent with how the event was being interpreted by the Child.

A thought is a decision of Mind. It's a Subconscious Truth. There's nothing wrong with the thoughts of the Child. But thoughts become beliefs. And beliefs decide what we get in life. So, ask the Child, "What does life look like, from now on, as a result of this experience?" This will reveal what the Child expects in the future. That's the belief.

Bring in Adult Consciousness to evaluate. How might these decisions have resulted in emotional reactivity? Hyper-sensitivity? Aggression? Unwanted symptoms? The word decide comes from the Latin *decidere* meaning "to cut off from." Cutting away everything, unlike love, will restore peace and clarity of Mind (hair).

This is a process of gently undoing erroneous beliefs, which resulted in defensive coping strategies (nails) and vulnerability to triggering. This will empower the client to make newer, better decisions for themself, independent of external conditions and the opinions of others. The client can decide what they will keep. The rest can be let go.

Forgiveness is a letting go. Having dealt with their feelings and needs, the client recognizes that they had no choice but to distract or avoid whenever they were feeling upset or unhappy. It was a question of survival for them as a Child. But being brave and playing nice to please others got them into trouble (through no fault of their own). Gratifying our parents' unconscious needs came at the cost of our own self-realization. Pretending to be a tough little soldier was necessary for the Child, but hiding our truest feelings comes at great cost.

This needs to be brought to consciousness, acknowledged, and mourned. Grieving the loss of childhood will result in self-compassion so that authentic self-forgiveness can occur. Forgiving the Child will set the client free from the pattern of masking pain, hiding behind achievements, seeking solace in substances, and pretending to be someone they're not. Restoring the Child to their natural state of goodness washes the client clean. So, encourage the client to feel forgiveness toward their younger self fully, deeply, and completely. Saturate the client with positive feelings of compassion toward themself. Then, amplify it with feelings of accomplishment, peace, gratitude, love, and appreciation and encourage the client to take ownership of these changes. *You did that!*

#4. Seal It – Restore Goodness

A child doesn't need to do anything to be worthy of love and acceptance. Every child is intrinsically loveable and deserves only love and acceptance. Because the Child is a Part of the client, accepting and forgiving the Child is an act of self-forgiveness. So, the place to begin the Forgiveness Work is always with the Child.

All forgiveness is self-forgiveness. When support, love and acceptance are given by the Adult Part to the Child Part, it is an act of self-love and self-acceptance. This forgiveness will set the Child free to grow up, knowing that they are worthy of love. In doing so, the client gives themself permission to move forward with their life, no longer defined by the things of the past.

Past events define who we think we are. When hurts are unforgiven, it leaves the client feeling like a Victim of Circumstance, powerless because of the wounds of the past. Survivor Identity is not a position of strength. There's no wisdom in having merely endured a traumatic experience. Something must be gained for having had the experience.

When a Child gets hurt, the tendency is for the Child to take the blame, especially when the Offender is a parent. Blaming the parent puts the

Child at risk of abandonment or punishment. This generates fear, guilt, and shame. Releasing the fear will bring relief. With the pressure gone, physical tension will begin to relax. The client will finally be able to breathe again. As a result, they will be able to look at the event with calm confidence. With your help, the client can come to realize that their feelings were not irrational. They were based on the perceptions, knowledge, and understanding of a Child. The Child simply lacked the maturity needed to cope with the situation. That's forgivable.

If the Child did something wrong, made a mistake, or feels responsible for what Offender did to him, the Child will take the blame. With nowhere for the feelings to go, all the hurt, fear, and anger gets turned inward, seeding guilt.

When the blame gets turned inward, feelings of anger, condemnation, and rejection will generate anxiety, which can express through physical or emotional symptoms. When projected outward (denial), it can result in interpersonal conflicts (war) and vulnerability to further triggering.

If Adult is blaming the Child for what happened, the Child will feel it, adding to the unresolved Pain Package. What the Adult needs to accept is that human beings learn through trial and error. Human beings make mistakes. In the movies, a mistake requires a do-over, not condemnation. A mistake is an opportunity to learn, choose differently, do better, and grow in resourcefulness, strength, and wisdom to live a more fulfilling life.

As we relinquish the need to be perfect, we accept our innate goodness as an evolving human soul. So, what the client needs to accept is that the Child is blameless. Whatever happened, it's not their fault. There is nothing a Child could ever do to deserve ill-treatment. A child is vulnerable and dependent on others for his survival. What the Child needed in that situation was love and protection. That didn't happen.

To heal, the Adult needs to give love and acceptance to the Child.

With understanding comes compassion toward the Child. That's forgiveness. The greater the understanding, the more compassion is experienced. This experience of forgiveness will make it easier for the client to face and forgive others. It's simply easier to forgive the Child than the people who hurt them. And this will give the client an experience of how good it feels to forgive.

Clients often describe the experience as having found themselves, gratitude, compassion, acceptance, and love toward self and others. Physically, the client may be feeling calm and relaxed. Mentally, the client may be realizing greater clarity, insight, confidence, and peace of mind. Emotionally, they may be allowing a new sense of optimism, happiness, freedom, aliveness, and gratitude to flow through them. These are the gifts of forgiveness.

Friedrich Nietzsche wrote, "That which does not kill me makes me stronger." Once the Child has been washed clean and saturated with love and forgiveness in the ISE, gather up all the benefits of change and give them back to the client through direct suggestion with "Now you know" statements. Build a strong case for having been transformed by this experience. For example, "You've changed. From now on, you're allowed to grow in strength and wisdom, knowing that you are forgiven for all your mistakes. You have given yourself a wonderful gift, here, today. This empowers you to move forward in the knowledge that only what is loving is true. Notice how good that feels."

#1. Find It

Wisdom has been defined as the past cleansed of negative emotions. In alchemy, this is referred to as the transmutation of lead to gold. The experience must be transformed into a growth-experience. True strength and wisdom are a by-product of cleansing the past of negative emotions to find the gifts in the garbage.

Invite the client to look at that event one last time, only this time they see it through the eyes of love. Then, give the suggestion that "every cloud has a silver lining" or "with every curse comes a blessing." In other words, it's possible to find good in our past experiences, no matter how challenging. What good can the client find for having been through that experience? What did they learn that could help them to grow in strength, wisdom, and kindness? How might knowing what they know now change things from now on? How might this knowledge benefit them in the future?

#2. Feel It

Each learning is a Thought that forms a new decision about the client's way of being in the world from now on. There's no such thing as a neutral thought. A positive thought will elicit a positive emotion. So, how does that make the client feel? Make a list! These are nuggets of gold. Gather them up so that you can give them back to the client as direct suggestions.

#3. Heal It

Elicit a commitment from the client to keep all these learnings and better feelings. Then, grow the Child up to Adulthood, through the SSEs, bringing this new level of wisdom and understanding with them. Only this time, the Child gets to grow up knowing what it's like to be loved and accepted. As this happens, they can remember what happened in the past, but only the love, strength, and wisdom gained for having been through those experiences goes with them.

Once you have grown the Child up and integrated all changes at the level of Adult Consciousness, the client is ready to face the Offender and take back their power. The client can clearly see how it was for them as a Child. As a Child, they saw through the eyes of a Child. They thought like a Child and felt like a Child. But they're not a Child anymore. They're a Grownup, now, able to make their own decisions and live their life free of the past.

#4. Seal It

Facing the Offender requires Adult Consciousness. It's the Adult Consciousness of the client that needs to forgive, not the Child. While past experiences caused the Child pain, it's the Adult who carries the burden of accumulated, unresolved hurt, resentment, anger, and vengeance. To truly forgive requires Adult Wisdom. So, once the process of integrating and generalizing change at the Adult level is complete, the final task is to prepare the Adult to face and forgive the Offender.

Adult Consciousness is a by-product of many years of experience. Now that the past influences have been resolved, the grime of self-blame, guilt, and shame have been transformed into the grit of courage and strength of character. Finding good in painful past experiences results in a fundamental change in how the client sees themself – their identity. For example, when a client accepts the identity of a non-smoker, the smoking behavior is no longer congruent with how they see himself. This results in effortless permanence to the change in behavior.

This is what Forgiveness Work is about. It's about realizing a real and lasting result. Through grieving the losses of childhood, removing the self-blame, and recognizing how past experiences taught the client how to be in order to survive, the client is no longer bound to the past. They realize that the people who were supposed to take care of them, protect them, and keep them whole didn't know how to do that. Regardless of what might have happened, it doesn't change the fact of who they are at their Core.

Allowing the Child inside the Adult to grow up means that there is finally a Grownup who can stand up for the Child, speak for them, act on their behalf, and demand their right to be. The client is now ready to face the Offender and assert their value as a worthy human soul.

Adult Forgiveness

When the devil was finished, he gave Hans back his backpack full of sweepings and said, "Now go and tell the innkeeper to give you back your gold. Tell him, if he doesn't, he'll end up tending the fires in your place."

The innkeeper is the Offender, the "One Person who hurt the client more than anyone." Usually, this is a parent, but not always. Whoever he might be, the devil knows that any small bit of grievance the client might harbor will only keep them bound and, as a result, vulnerable to the Offender's behavior, attitudes, words, criticism, etc.

Forgiveness is the healing. If the Offender does not relinquish their control over the client's self-worth, there will be no forgiveness. In this case, more work will be required to get to the underlying cause. So, the client is reminded of how much work they have invested in getting free of the past. The Offender has the power to influence how the client feels, not because of what they did but because the client has internalized this person. Psychologically, the client is sleeping with the enemy! But no matter how vile, they are still a Part of the client and, as such, deserves to be forgiven.

To truly be free of the past, the client must reclaim their authentic power by releasing their emotional attachment to the Offender. To do this, the client must be prepared to face the person who hurt them and take back their power. It takes a strong ego to face the Offender. The Adult Consciousness cannot be contaminated by the fears and vulnerabilities of the Child. Ego Strengthening suggestions can be offered here to fill the client with resources to empower him to face the innkeeper.

I have a couple of poems I like to adapt for ego-strengthening purposes. One is *Desiderata,* which states, "You are a child of the Universe, no less than the trees and the stars. You have a right to be here." The other is Virginia Satir's *Declaration of Self-Esteem.* If you're an Omni-grad you'll recognize this as the "You are You" patter. From these, I have created a script that I use to set up for forgiveness work.

You can download a copy of it here: www.tribeofhealers.com/download-devils-therapy-forgiveness-script

If you're like me, you were taught the standard Forgiveness Protocol, which emphasizes convincing the client that forgiveness is a good idea. But what's been causing the client pain is all the unresolved emotional energies trapped inside. Anger doesn't feel good. And *repressed* anger is a killer.

While understanding more cognitive approaches to forgiveness can certainly help you *prepare* a client to allow forgiveness to happen, the healing lies in the emotional release work. Forgiveness is not something that we *do*. It's something that happens when you let go of negative emotions. Release everything, unlike love, and you won't have to convince the client to do anything. The forgiveness will happen automatically. To accomplish this, the client must be willing to release all the anger toward the Offender.

In his book, *Forgive for Good*, Dr. Fred Luskin presents nine steps to forgiveness. Luskin's first step corresponds with steps one and two of the Universal Healing Process: (1) Know exactly how you *feel* about what happened, and (2) Express what about the situation is not okay. In other words, find the feeling, then feel it to release it. Luskin's next step is to recognize that forgiveness is for *you* and no one else. This is an important understanding because forgiveness is a choice that only the client can make.

A battle has been raging in the client's Mind, generating the symptoms. War is the result of perceiving that someone has done something unforgivable. Forgiveness is a letting go. Letting go of the anger restores peace – physically, mentally, and emotionally. To accomplish this, the client needs to understand what it means to forgive.

The Buddha said that the root of all suffering is attachment. What we judge good we want, and it enslaves us. What we judge bad is bound to us, through fear, and has the power to control us. Complete healing requires complete forgiveness. Forgiveness that is only partial or halfhearted won't get the job done. You can't leave a little infection in the wound. It's only going to fester. Each thought of vengeance toward the Offender becomes an act of self-punishment. Whoever the client has been blaming for their pain – the lieutenant, sergeant, father, mother, spouse, boss, sibling, etc. – is an image in their *Mind.* Forgiving the people who hurt them will set the client free of the power they have held over them.

When the client can look upon the Offender and see them as forgivable, *their own self-concept changes.* Remember, the Offender is an Internal Representation of how the Child perceived the Offender in the ISE. What's hurting the client *now* is holding onto past grievances in the form of anger, resentment, blame, and condemnation. This is a self-punishment program. The client has been punishing himself, in the privacy of his own Mind, by holding onto the pain of the past. Worse, all the unresolved toxic emotional debris from the past has been contaminating the client's present life and all their relationships! And because they have internalized the people who hurt them, *until* they forgive, they will continue to suffer the symptoms.

The devil restores the client's gold to them by reminding the client of how they got all their good feelings back. They've changed. Releasing uncomfortable feelings has allowed them to feel good about themself again. They're not a Child, anymore. As a grown-up, they're allowed to feel all their feelings and express them in healthier ways. These suggestions are congruent with the client's internal experience of the healing process. This makes them true.

If the Offender is still in the client's daily life (e.g., spouse, parent, boss, etc.), the client is reminded that even though they've changed, the Offender hasn't. The client is now free to feel good about themselves despite how the Offender might be. While events in the past caused the client to think and feel and respond in ways they didn't like, releasing the past sets them free to choose their responses *from now on.*

Forgiveness is a letting go. Letting go of the emotional baggage attached to the Offender will empower the client to begin to live from a place of wholeness; where they have a positive sense of themself and others, and where, no matter what life sends at them, they can feel good about themself, life, and the world around them.

When forgiveness is complete, and there's nothing left to forgive, there's nothing to re-infect the Mind or support the symptoms. Simply put – forgiveness is the healing. All that's required is the willingness to forgive. But to be willing to forgive, the client needs to understand what forgiveness is NOT.

What Forgiveness is NOT

Forgiveness is NOT for the person who hurt you. The only person who will benefit is you. Your forgiveness does not change the Offender's life one iota. If the Offender is still alive, they have to live with themself. You no longer have to. You have punished yourself long enough for the things that thy did. Allow yourself to claim back all the energy you've been wasting on thoughts and feelings that only cause you pain. Forgiveness means taking back your power and allowing love to flow back into your life.

If deceased, the Offender's life is over. Regardless, punishing yourself with feelings of regret, vengeance, resentment, and other destructive emotions rooted in the past changes nothing for him. It only keeps you stuck in the pain of the past. Forgiveness isn't for the Offender. It's for you and no one else.

Forgiveness does NOT mean condoning what was done. It does not excuse bad behavior or minimize how you were impacted. The Offender hurt you. That was wrong. But choosing to hold onto painful feelings only keeps a person stuck in their own personal Groundhog Day where the things that happened in the past continue to control them in their daily life. That's no way to live!

Some people's thoughts are so focused on the past that they rob themselves of a true present. They miss out on all the happiness that's waiting for them because all the painful feelings from the past – regret, resentment, hate, and guilt – continue to hold them hostage. As a result, they feel powerless to create a better, more satisfying future. You have a choice. Forgiveness is not condoning what happened. It recognizes that it's over so that you can take back your life.

Forgiveness does NOT mean denying what happened. Forgiveness is not denial. Living in denial just keeps a person stuck in *hoping* for a better future without ever taking steps to change it. Forgiveness is facing the truth of the past and recognizing that you have suffered long enough. The past is the past. And there's no future in the past.

Forgiveness does NOT mean having to tell the Offender that you have forgiven him. Forgiveness isn't for him. It's for you. You decide. This is a mature understanding of what it means to forgive. Forgiveness is a choice to put an end to the suffering by setting yourself free. You don't have to invite him back into your life if you don't want to. You don't have to tell him a thing. The only person who needs to know that you have forgiven is you.

Forgiveness does not mean forgetting what happened. Historians tell us that if we fail to learn from our past, we are destined to repeat it. As a result, we suffer. Your history has value because of what you learned from it. Forgiveness allows you to choose to see the past as a *learning experience,* find some good in it, and move forward in life, feeling stronger and wiser because of it. Forgiveness is not forgetting. It is remembering in a way that empowers you.

Summary

In *The Prospering Power of Love,* Catherine Ponder wrote that release and forgiveness are aspects of love. Through release and forgiveness, we break up, cross out, dissolve, and are freed forever from the negative attitudes and memories that have limited us. She states that emotional release is one of the highest forms of love.

True forgiveness is a natural *expression* of Love. It begins with the Child because, at our Core, that is what we are – Love. When we come back into alignment with our Core Energy, forgiveness happens naturally. As we release old grievances, we come to accept others *as they are,* without needing them to change, while retaining our right to peace and freedom. This restores our ability to love and accept *ourselves,* just as we are.

To forgive is to find the good. This is reflected in the biblical story of Joseph, who, no matter what woes befell him, would say, "God meant it for good." It's when you realize that no wrong has been done, that you survived, that you can begin to look for a silver lining. This is a forgiveness that requires Adult Consciousness. It is based on the understanding that healing does not stop things from going wrong in life. It just means giving up the Pain Story about how life has been treating us.

As long as the client has a need to sing his "Another Somebody Done Somebody Wrong Song," he remains bound to the Offender. To be genuinely free of the past, the client must let go of the old Story about how they were wronged. The Offender must be viewed as merely human, not a character in a soap opera, or worse, a monster.

When you hold resentment against anyone, you are bound to that person by a cosmic link, a real, though mental chain. You are tied by a cosmic tie to the thing you hate. The one person perhaps in the whole world whom you most dislike, is the very one to whom you are attaching yourself by a hook that is stronger than steel. - **Emmet Fox**

CHAPTER 20:
Release & Reclaim

H ans did as he was instructed. He went up to the Innkeeper and said, "You stole my money. If you don't give it back, you'll go to hell in my place. And you'll look every bit as horrible as I did."

Facing the Offender involves releasing the grievance and reclaiming power by recovering what was lost as a result of those experiences. This begins with establishing an environment where it's safe for the client to be themself. For example, if the Offender is a loved one, a safe environment might be the kitchen.

If the client is a gardener, or if the Offender is deceased, a garden scene works well. A campfire or beach scene is a nice option for outdoorsy types. The Grey Room is a generic, one-size-fits-all scenario that can be adapted to Forgiveness Work. The Grey Room is a circular, soft grey room with a domed ceiling, like an igloo. At the center of the room are two chairs facing each other. The client sits comfortably in one chair. The Offender sits in the other chair. This sets up for a dialogue process.

To begin, the Offender does not have the right to speak. Only the client can speak. If the Offender is a particularly *nasty* character, you can suggest restraints. (I like to duct-tape them to the chair.) The important point is that the client has all the power. The Offender cannot speak, cannot move, cannot do anything. All the Offender can do is listen. What follows, then, is a process of therapeutic blaming. For this reason, I like to use a Red Room because seeing red suggests anger.

The client is encouraged to assert themselves by telling the Offender how what they did hurt the client and how this impacted them. The client then tells the Offender how this experience has affected them growing up and in the present life (i.e., the symptoms). The client reviews the Offender's *crimes* like a prosecutor in a trial, allowing the client to get it out verbally.

Blaming the Offender allows forbidden truths to finally be given voice. This will bring authentic feelings of hurt, anger, sadness, and fear to the surface where they can be purged. This process of getting it out involves both speaking or shouting while releasing the emotional charge attached to the Offender.

Speaking the truth of how it was for the client in each of these events will validate the feelings, encouraging more emotions to come to the surface to be released. Tapping or pumping the feelings into a pillow discharges the energy trapped in the body's nervous system.

Release is a form of forgiveness. — **Catherine Ponder**

Release the Grievance

During the Middle Ages, the church set out to purge the land of Gnostics (those who seek to know God directly). In France, local noblemen were paid to take up arms against the Cathars, who were viewed as a threat to the Catholic Church's authority as the go-between, God, and man. The problem was that Cathars looked pretty much like everyone else. There was no way to separate heretics from good Catholics! A solution was agreed upon. *Kill them all; let God sort them out.*

This is precisely what we must do – focus on purging all the feelings that got trapped inside. This actually makes forgiveness work relatively simple. The only decision we need to make – get it out! Get it *all* out! Anger needs a way out. Resentment needs a way out. Disappointment needs a way out, as does sadness, fear, and hurt. Every uncomfortable feeling trapped inside needs to be felt fully and released. The pillow is the perfect place for this. Any uncomfortable feeling can be pumped into the pillow, but big feelings like anger are more easily released when you use bigger movements.

The releasing process begins with the statement, "You hurt me." This is a general statement of truth. It's a warm-up. But the goal is to bring to light specific offenses. Remember, the devil is in the details. The more specific you can be, the better your results will be. This is where your session notes can support you in getting a complete resolution of the client's issue. If there were multiple events involving the same Offender, the SSEs give you a list of grievances to work through. Start with the ISE and work your way through the SSEs to the present time.

Have the client think back to the ISE and state, "You hurt me when I was [insert age]." Then, have the client tell the Offender what they did to cause pain. Release everything that's still trapped in the timeline.

Pumping anger into a pillow will bring rapid relief. Just find the feeling.

Feel the feeling. And *put the feeling in the pillow* – all of it.

What happened? How did this make the client feel? What did it make them think about themself, others, life? The more the client is able to admit and experience their truest feelings, the stronger and more coherent they will feel. This will enable the client to expose themselves to emotions that well up out of their earliest childhood and to experience the helplessness and uncertainty of that period of his life. What decisions were made because of those experiences? How did the decisions made at that time result in problems growing up? How is this still a problem for the client?

Releasing anger tends to occur in rounds. The client will release a layer, then rest briefly before allowing the next wave to present itself. Just keep pumping the feeling into the pillow. This is uncomfortable work so remind the client that there's only so much of it in there by encouragingly saying, "Get it out! You're going to feel so good!"

When a feeling is exhausted, something will have changed. So, give the client a moment to rest and recalibrate. Then, have them go inside and notice what has changed. Whatever has shifted, bring awareness to it, and validate it. Every validation of release is a *sweeping*. It's a recognition of change that will accrue dividends. Just set it aside, behind the door, as an installment toward forgiveness, then go back inside and check to see if there's anything left. Wash, rinse, repeat.

When the energy is completely exhausted, there will be no anger towards the Offender. Check carefully. Is it *all* gone? If so, instruct the client to focus on the Offender and notice how they, the client, feel. If the grievance has been neutralized, the client will report feeling one of the following:

- Neutral
- Peaceful
- Love
- Gratitude
- Compassion
- Happy
- Alive

If the client says that they feel *empty or nothing*, I verify that the emotional charge has, in fact, been neutralized. Ask, "Is that a *good* empty feeling . . . or a *bad* empty feeling?" Bad feelings need to be released.

If it seems like all the negative energy has been released, instruct the client to focus on how the body feels now. Is the anger gone? Is it *all* gone? If so, instruct the client to notice how it feels to say these words, "I forgive you [the Offender]. I set you free." This is the test for forgiveness.

The Forgiveness Test

While releasing deep emotional wounds can take time, intention, and effort, forgiveness can happen in a heartbeat. When it does, a change of heart occurs that will bring the client deep and lasting relief. The test for forgiveness is not the words, however. The test is how it feels to forgive. Any residual block or unresolved grievance will only reseed the problem. Release must be complete.

If the forgiveness statement doesn't feel good or true, there's still something unresolved. The body doesn't lie. If anger remains, continue releasing with, "I still feel [insert emotion, e.g., angry] because [put an ending on it]." Encourage the client to release every block to *allow* forgiveness by making it reasonable for the client to forgive. For example:

- To forgive means simply to set free, to liberate, by giving up what you don't want (the negative), so you can have what you do want (the positive).

- Releasing the *bad* feeling brings relief, allowing *good* to flow back into your life – physically, mentally, and emotionally.

- Forgiveness only benefits you. It's not for the Offender. It's for you and *your* healing.

- Unforgiveness – blame, anger, condemnation, and hurt – make the mind a living hell. Holding onto those feelings only keeps you stuck in the pain of the past. Get it out. Then, you'll know what it's like to be free. You'll feel it!

- Forgiving does not condone what the Offender did. Nor is it making excuses for their behavior. Whatever they did, whatever they said was *wrong*. But you don't have to keep punishing yourself because of those things. Get it out, and it's over.

- Forgiving does not mean you have to like this person. It's a recognition that the pain that was put in you was put inside the Offender in the same way. It doesn't belong to you. You get it out, and you're free to forgive and set yourself free.

- We're not making excuses for the Offender. Haven't you punished yourself long enough? Forgiveness is your choice to set yourself free by no longer punishing yourself for the things of the past. Get it out and set yourself free.

- You get it out, here and now, and the Offender out of your life.
  You'll feel it! You've rented out enough space to them in your Mind. They (have to/ have had to) live with themself. You no longer have to. Get it out and take back your power so you can move forward with your life.

- Forgiving makes *you* stronger. It's giving up feeling like a victim by setting you free of the control those things have had over you all these years. You get that out, and it changes everything!

- Forgiveness is your *get out of jail free* card. It doesn't change the past. It changes how you feel *inside*. No one's past has to be a prison sentence. Get it out and set yourself free.

- Forgiving the Offender sets *you* free to begin a new chapter in your life, free of the weight/burden/baggage/pain you've been carrying in your Mind and body. You get that out! You're going to feel so good!

In his book, The Sunflower, Simon Weisenthal tells a story about a Jew during WWII who is taken from the labor camp to the bedside of a dying Nazi. The Nazi wishes to confess his sins and receive forgiveness from a representative of the Jewish people. Much debate ensues regarding the authority to forgive on behalf of another. But the question is beside the point. The real question is whether you can forgive another for *yourself!* The need to understand and, therefore, qualify your forgiveness is merely a tool. It is not a pre-requisite. Either you want to be at peace, or you value the grievance.

Authentic forgiveness feels good! It's a letting go of the pain of the past. Unfortunately, too few people know what true forgiveness is. They try to forgive with the Thinking Mind. Head forgiveness never works. Real forgiveness comes from the heart. It's a feeling. That's what we're testing for.

Sometimes the client will forgive, but only partially. Sometimes a client will hold onto anger because they believe letting it go will leave them vulnerable to future hurt. Sometimes the client will hold onto sadness for fear they will lose their connection to a loved one. But partial forgiveness just won't get the job done. Complete and unconditional *forgiveness is the healing.*

If the client says, "I forgive you / I set you free," and it doesn't feel authentic to you, or you notice that there's tension still present, use autosuggestion to validate the client's willingness to forgive. For example, "I do feel better / I'm allowed to forgive and feel better / I'm learning / how to forgive / so I can set myself free / and heal / etc."

Then dig deeper to uncover the block to full forgiveness. For example, "Even though I forgive you / there's still something I need to forgive / So I can be completely free / I still can't forgive you completely because [insert an ending]." or "Something I still can't forgive is insert an ending]"

Additional Sentence Stems for uncovering grievances toward another include:

Something I want to tell you . . .

Something I'm angry about . . .

Something I resent you for . . .

The best thing I remember in our life together . . .

The worst thing I remember in our life together . . .

Something I'm ready to forgive you for . . .

Something I'm *not* ready to forgive you for . . .

Something I need from you right now is . . .

When the release is complete, the client will feel very peaceful. Sometimes, the client will report that they feel tired. That's okay. After all, it takes energy to release energy! You can reframe this perception very easily by asking, "True or false – you feel peaceful?" If true, you can validate the client's hard work with "Good job! You did that! Notice how good it feels!"

Releasing everything, unlike love, naturally creates a void waiting to be filled. If the client says that they feel empty, make sure that it's a good feeling. Ask the client to offer another word to describe *empty*. Sometimes this will reveal a deeper feeling of loss. If the client says that they feel clear, or complete, or relief, it's time to fill the void by pouring in direct suggestions.

Reclaim Wholeness

Not only did the innkeeper give Hans back his money, but some more besides, begging Hans to keep it a secret and not to tell anybody. So, now Hans is a rich man.

Whatever the client feels that they lost as a result of the Offender's actions is now recognized and reclaimed. During the releasing process, take note of how the actions (or inaction) of the Offender have cost the client. This will give you a list of qualities that the client needs to reclaim to finally be free of the past. You can then invite the client to face the Offender and state, "I give you back your pain. I take back my [fill in the blank]."

Giving back the pain suggests that the Offender, too, knows pain. This helps to make forgiveness more reasonable because that pain had to be in the Offender before they could inflict it upon the client. Taking back each positive quality acknowledges the loss of wholeness the client has endured, which can now be reclaimed. Positive qualities to reclaim include good feelings about myself: power, courage, confidence, innocence, trust, joy, self-worth, self-acceptance, love, freedom (to be, feel my feelings, love, and be loved), etc.

Now is the time to get creative by incorporating other techniques into your process. For example, you can tap in the positive aspects, breathe in each new quality, give it color, and bring it into the heart. Use all the senses to reclaim what was lost and restore to the client his self-worth and self-authority.

Once the process of reclaiming is complete, the Offender's actions can be reframed as mistakes. Human beings make mistakes. Mistakes are how we learn. People can be unkind, either knowingly or unknowingly. Random events happen whether we like them or not. And if the person who hurt the client is still in his life, their behavior won't suddenly change just so the client can be happy.

Healing does not change *out there*. The client must consciously choose to relinquish any *unrealistic expectations* that the Offender is any different than there are. Fortunately, forgiveness doesn't require the Offender to change. Forgiveness is the change. It's a change in how the client feels *inside* that comes with realizing life isn't perfect, human beings make mistakes, and shit happens.

Forgiveness is a letting go. When the client lets go of the need for things to be other than how they were and accepts things as they are, they'll be free. This is important because the client needs to stop beating themselves up over the Offender's mistakes. When the client gives up the false hope that someday the Offender might change, behave differently, or treat them better, the client can give the Offender permission to live life; however, the client needs to without having to wait for that day for the Offender to find their own peace.

The client can remind the Offender (and themself) of what it took for them to find their peace. But when the Offending spouse, parent, or boss hasn't yet faced his or her own past, it's unlikely that this person will change until they do their own work of self-healing. This understanding releases the client from any other unrealistic expectations.

If the Offender is not sorry for what they did, there's still a power issue. The client has felt so vulnerable to the person who hurt them that they don't feel safe letting go of the grievance. Release the fear. Remember, even when the Offender exists in the client's outer life, they exist as an Internal Representation in the client's Mind. Unconsciously, the client is handing over the power to control how they feel. This must end. All that is required for the client to be free of the influence the Offender has had over them is to realize that whatever happened, whatever was said or done to them, it wasn't personal.

Parents have problems; they weren't the client's problems. Spouses have problems that were there long before they even met. Bosses have problems that have nothing to do with the client, never did. The only problem is that the client happened to be there when they had the problem. This understanding will allow the client to cut all negative emotional ties and, in the process, learn from the *Offender's* mistakes, as well as their own.

When release is complete, the client will feel it. They'll feel the peace and freedom that comes with having forgiven. You can then use the Forgiveness Test to verify that forgiveness is complete. "I forgive you. I set you free. As I set you free, I set myself free." Then, add, "I forgive you because [insert an ending]." This is a suggestion you want to compound powerfully. These are the client's own reasons for letting go of the problem! So, invite the client to repeat it multiple times, each time putting a different ending on it. "I forgive you because . . .put an ending on it." This is employing the Direct Drive Technique to reinforce the client's acceptance of having set themselves free.

Some people are difficult to forgive. Sometimes the Offender will show no remorse. When this happens, you have your work cut out for you. I was taught to just send the Offender to hell if they showed no remorse. In some cases, this can be a strategy that allows the client to express vengeance. But if you leave the Offender in hell, it just buries the problem deeper. Some people take a perverse pleasure in holding onto anger, hate, and condemnation. It gives them a false sense of power. They don't realize what holding onto negative thought, and emotional energies do to the Mind. It makes the Mind a living hell!

While condemning the Offender to hell may satisfy the client's need for vengeance, they're sentencing themselves to hell just so that they can keep roasting Offender on a spit.

Forgiveness is a by-product of the releasing. If the Offender won't give back the gold by expressing remorse, if they're not sorry for what they did, find a way to make them vulnerable and weak. The weakest and most vulnerable state is that of the infant. Anyone who has ever held an infant knows this. If you have ever nursed or bottle-fed an infant, you also know how a baby's eyes stare directly into your eyes. Eye contact is a primary means through which human beings communicate needs and wants. This imagery sets the stage for Gerald Kein's *Windows of the Soul Technique*, which gives you a way to make the Offender small and defenseless. It also gives you a way to find some good in the Offender.

The eyes are likened to the windows of the heart. - **Mark 7:20-23 (KJV)**

Windows of the Soul Technique

Begin with the suggestion that the eyes are the windows to the Soul. By looking deeply into a person's eyes, you can see into a person's past. The deeper you look into their eyes, the further back into their history you see.

Next, invite the client to look into the Offender's eyes so *deeply* that they can see all the way back to when she was just a baby in someone's arms. Verify that the client has this image. Then, go to work establishing a series of truisms that have already been established through the regression work. For example, every newborn baby deserves love.

If the client can agree that *that* baby is loveable, and that all a baby wants, or needs, is to love and be loved, you can build a case for ongoing forgiveness toward this person. Feelings don't come out of nowhere. This is a basic principle that the client has already accepted. Therefore, something must have happened to cause that child to lose her good feelings about herself. This recognizes that the Offender has suffered a loss, making her more forgivable and, therefore, good.

The things that were said or done to the Offender, growing up, caused her to feel bad inside. (The client recognizes this from his own history.) It was *this pain* that caused the Offender to act in ways that were hurtful toward the client. (Making the Offender a *victim* of her past, vulnerable to the people who hurt her, makes the Offender more forgivable.)

Growing up into adulthood, the Offender had to carry *all that emotional baggage from childhood.* (Generating a little sympathy for the Offender.) Even though she might have wanted to act in loving ways, she just wasn't *able* to overcome all the anger and hurt and pain inside. (Making the Offender appear weak and suffering in pain).

It was all the pain trapped inside of the Offender that caused her to act in ways that were unloving toward the client. (Making forgiveness reasonable.) This doesn't make what she did right. It's just understanding that *it wasn't the Offender's fault.* Something happened to make her act that way. Behind every action, there's a positive intention. While the Offender's underlying intention, no matter how twisted, was to feel good, she had no choice but to act in accordance with her internal programming. (Making the Offender a victim.)

When the client can look into the Offender's eyes and see a need that the Offender had hoped to fill through the client, the client will be able to see the Offender as weak and needy. This will allow the client to begin to see the Offender's behavior as a call for help. When the client can see the call for help, he can become the one to answer it. This opens the door to forgiveness.

When the client can state that he no longer has any need to punish the Offender, he is free of the past and, therefore, free to stop punishing himself in his own Mind. This sets him free to live as he now chooses – with or without this person. While the client is allowed to hope for the day that the Offender finds their peace, the client is no longer waiting for that day to come so that he can be happy. This is true freedom. When the Offender expresses remorse, authentic forgives occurs. This restores the security and deservedness that is the true gold of the heart.

More Besides . . .

There's a touch of Matthew in the Grimm's tale that says, "If a man asks you for something, give him more than he asks." The reason behind this is that when you give, you benefit. The more you forgive, the more you are forgiven. All forgiveness is self-forgiveness.

If the Offender is a loved one, ask if there is anything that they need to forgive the client for. Even if there's nothing to forgive, guide the Offender to say the words, "I forgive you. I set you free. I forgive you because [insert an ending]." This allows the Offender to give more besides by adding to the client's overall sense of self-worth and deservedness in life.

The overall experience can then be further enriched by giving the client a few minutes to soak up the good feelings resulting from forgiveness. To deepen the transformation, ask the client what they have learned because, often, what follows complete forgiveness is a cascade of insights or realizations that can enrich the client in ways you never imagined! For example, the client might realize that:

- An abusive parent wanted to be loving but didn't know how.

- The client was actually wanted and loved.

- What happened wasn't personal; it was just the fact that they happened to be there.

These kinds of insights can transform a person's life for good!

Self-Forgiveness

I remember a scene from a movie in which Tom Selleck plays the role of the town sheriff, Jesse Stone. In this particular scene, the city council has called a meeting to reprimand Stone because they disapprove of his methods. Stone's response? "You can fire me, but you can't tell me what to do." That's authentic power.

It's recognizing the facts of the situation without giving up your power. It's not about being better than or less than. It's about taking a stand and standing your ground. Forgiveness restores this power, allowing you to accept the past by recognizing that everything in your history made you who you are today.

Forgiveness means being okay with it – all of it. Ultimately, it's about respecting yourself. When you deeply and completely love and accept yourself, you don't let other people walk all over you or treat you like dirt. You can demand respect. If they refuse, they can go to hell without you choosing to join them.

When the Offender repents, the client reclaims what they lost through painful encounters in the past. What they lost was their sense of self-respect and self-worth. This is the basis of shame. Shame is the belief that you are broken and flawed, that there is something missing within you. Shame is a Great Lie accepted by the Child. Forgiveness is the correction.

Guilt says that I *made* a mistake. Shame personalizes it. *I AM a mistake.* This is an identity issue calling for correction. Forgiveness corrects this letting go of false identification with the internal representation. The client is now free to forgive themselves forever putting themselves in harm's way, forever being vulnerable or unaware, for making mistakes. In other words, for being a Child. This restores the client to their innocence. As a result, they can now see the Truth.

The client could not have predicted what was going to happen. Nothing in life could have prepared them for any of it. And even though stuff happened, it's over. The client is stronger and wiser because of it. Despite it all, nothing could ever change the Truth about the client; that they are, and they remain, as they were created – a worthy soul on an important journey. This is what it means to be a rich man.

Summary

Forgiveness is a natural by-product of releasing trapped emotions, particularly anger. Anger is good. Anger gives you power when you need to defend yourself and others. What's not good is holding onto anger. When anger gets trapped inside, it generates dis-ease.

Anger is there to motivate you to protect yourself and the people or things you care about by establishing healthy boundaries. Protection is the Subconscious Mind's Prime Directive. If the client can consciously take responsibility for their own safety, the Subconscious Mind won't have to. As a result, it will relax, allowing the Conscious Mind to have what it wants— control.

Allowing anger to be felt and expressed provides the client with the energy needed to stand up for their rights. Standing up to the person who hurt you and saying, "You don't get to control me! You no longer have any power over me!" gets the anger out. It is an expression of self-assertiveness that puts an end to the Victim Identity. That's what's needed.

Like every phase in the healing process, facing the Offender involves the four healing steps:

1. **Find it.** Find the anger.
2. **Feel it.** Express the blame and anger authentically without holding back.
3. **Heal it.** Take back what was taken (power, self-worth, self-respect, innocence, etc.).
4. **Seal it.** Make it permanent. How does finally getting it off your chest change things?

CHAPTER 21:
A Real & Lasting Result

He started on the way home to his father and bought himself a coarse white coat.

Releasing creates space for something good to get in. Reclaiming what was lost through painful encounters in the past restores to the client what has been lacking within them – the power of choice. When the Offender chooses to forgive the client, the client is giving themselves *more besides*.

Letting go of the Pain Story transforms how the client sees themself. Because they are no longer bound to experiences and people from the past, they are is no longer bound to the Victim Identity that has roots in the powerlessness of the Child. Where they were once a lost *soul-dier* without means, they are now grown to adulthood, free to consciously choose a new identity and way of being in the world.

A New You

When you change the outcome of a past wounding event, it changes the client's expectations for the future. So, once the Forgiveness Work is complete, Future Pacing (a.k.a. Age Progression) is the final test of the results. Whatever occurs in the future scene is the client's promise to themselves of what they are living into.

If the client has a happy journey into the future, this gives them an experience of what it will be like to be living life free of the past. The ability to imagine themselves responding differently to situations that, in the past, were impossible to cope with can be an empowering experience that changes how the client sees themself.

If the issue is completely resolved, Future Pacing will allow the client to pay it forward by projecting the benefits of change into the future. This establishes a powerful expectation of life looks like from now on. The experience of moving effortlessly through situations that, in the past, were overwhelming provides evidence that something has changed. You can use this realization to generate insights. The world hasn't changed. The people around the client haven't changed. Situations in daily life haven't changed. What has changed is *the client*. That's the insight you're looking for!

White is traditionally associated with spirituality and purification, indicating that the client's new self-image is realistic. The client assumes an ordinary role. They are not expecting to be better-than or less-than anyone else. They are simply themself. They're okay with that. This is a realistic self-image and, by extension, a realistic expectation toward life. Now that the client knows how they got here, they are now free to chart a new course for themselves and create a better future based on what they learned through the healing process. They have no further need to strive to be perfect. They are enough. And because their worthiness is no longer defined by externals, they are now empowered to be more successful in life.

You have power over your mind—not outside events. Realize this, and you will find strength. – **Marcus Aurelius**

Play It Forward

As he went on his way, he played music for he had learned how to do that from the devil in hell.

The devil takes many forms. One of them is Pan, the great nature god of ancient Greece. The word pan means "all, every, whole." Pan was born with hooves and horns, but he was never evil, merely horny. He was a playful spirit who lived in the woods. But if you dared to disturb his peace during nap-time, his angry shouts would inspire *panic*. The word pandemic also tracks back to the god Pan. As the god of sound, Pan is frequently depicted playing an instrument he fashioned out of reeds called the Pan Flute.

In ancient philosophy, sound is the basis of everything in the universe. Music is a sound that both evokes and expresses emotion. Emotion is the language of the Subconscious Mind. This is what the client learned in hell– how to feel their truest feelings. They have no further need for suppression, repression, or depression to survive. That's no way to live!

As an Empowered Adult, the client must take responsibility for meeting their own emotional needs. By giving themselves permission to feel uncomfortable emotions like fear, anger, and sadness, the client is now able to experience and express true happiness. Happiness is the emotional satisfaction of having our needs met. But happiness that is dependent on other people and things is always subject to disappointment. This keeps us forever bound to seeking pleasure and avoiding pain.

Joy, on the other hand, is happiness that is independent of externals. Joy is not really an emotion. It's an energy that we experience as a way of being. As a result, it can always be there– even when faced with adversity. Hypnosis mentor, Michael Ellner, described this way of being as "A peaceful mind, a happy heart, and a playful spirit." It's a flow of well-being that brings greater love, wisdom, or strength.

As these qualifies grow lighter and stronger within the client, they fill their heart like a song. And when the heart feels full, it naturally radiates positive energy to every cell in the body. As the client expresses love to no one in particular, it goes out to the whole universe and echoes back to themself. Expressing positive feelings benefits everyone.

The client is now free to be happy or sad whenever anything makes them sad or happy. They don't have to look cheerful to please someone else. They don't have to suppress their feelings to fit other people's needs. They can feel anger knowing that no one will die because of it. The client is free to fully be themself.

To be happy, keep your heart free from hate, your mind from worry. Live simply, expect little, give much, Scatter sunshine, forget self, think of others. Try this for a week, and you will be surprised. –
Norman Vincent Peale

Age Progression

There was, however, an old king in that country, before whom he had to play. The king was so delighted with his playing that he promised Hans, his eldest daughter in marriage.

It is only after the client has liberated himself from the pain of the past that his true Self can begin to express and grow. And develop creatively. With this comes a new vitality. This is not a homecoming, however, because this home has never existed for the client. The new country they are now discovering is coming home to himself – their Future Self.

Age Progression allows the client to meet their Future Self. Just as the Inner Child is an Internal Representation of the client's younger self at a specific age, Future Self represents their older self sometime in the future. You can progress the client a few weeks, months, or even years to test their expectations for the future. Whatever occurs in the future scene is the client's promise to themselves of who they are becoming! So, invite a dialogue between these two Parts of the client.

Remember, Future Self knows everything about the client's life from now on. Who do they become? What gifts or talents have they developed? What do they know in the future that they don't know now? What advice can Future Self offer? What promise is Future Self making to the client? Any promise made by Future Self to the client constitutes a self-fulfilling prophecy. They are, after all, the same person!

But when the daughter heard that she was to be married to a lowborn fellow in a coarse white coat, she declared, "Before I do that, I'll jump into the deepest river."

Notice how this is a replay of meeting the innkeeper? The client is being judged not-good-enough. Just because the client has changed doesn't mean that person's behavior will change! So, if there is someone in the client's present life – a boss, a spouse, a parent – whose opinion holds weight, make sure you test the client's responses in an imagined future encounter with this person. For example, Darlene's husband is probably not going to quit drinking.

The client changes. Other people do not. But marital partners are often chosen because they are a match to what was familiar in childhood. An unresolved relationship with a Parent can be reflected in the client's current relationship with his or her spouse.

When the spouse has been cast in the role of surrogate Parent, the client will stay stuck in the role of Child struggling to get his needs met. When the old pattern is one of rejection, criticism, or abuse, that's what's familiar. So, you need to test the client's responses to their spouse's behavior. For example, what happens when Darlene's husband goes on a bender? What happens when he throws a tantrum, spews criticism and put-downs? Does she get emotionally triggered? Does she attempt to please? Does she hold onto the false expectation that her husband needs to change so she can be happy?

Others cannot be expected to change; the client must change. Remember, the person who shows up in a future scene isn't *out there*. They're an internal representation. If the client gets triggered, they are still vulnerable to the opinions of others. When that happens, go back to the Forgiveness Work. Put the Inner Critic in the hot seat, and encourage the client to give that Inner Critic a good talking to. Releasing this pattern of self-rejection, self-criticism, and self-abuse will allow your client to reclaim the power that has been given to this person.

Authentic Power

So, the king gives Hans his youngest daughter, who was willing to do it to please her father.

The client has completed the process of growing up. They have confronted their past, released the emotional grime, and reclaimed their right to self-rule. In forgiving the past, they have become their *own king*, their own authority, having reclaimed authentic power —the power of choice

Changing their responses has put the client back in control of their life. The client now believes that they are deserving of love and respect. Because they are willing to love and accept themself, warts, and all, they are no longer vulnerable to the opinions of others. When met with criticism and rejection, there is no emotional response. As a result, their Future Self offers them a better choice of more satisfying relationships. They are now empowered to move forward into a more satisfying and fulfilling future. This is a promise the client is making to themself. From now on, life will reward the client with what they deserve — acceptance and respect.

In *Power vs. Force*, David Hawkins suggests that willingness is the gateway to higher levels of awareness. But Spiritual Emergence calls for an appropriate vessel. The ancient healers recognized that, before one can access higher states, there is a need to purify oneself. Unresolved negative perceptions will only contaminate the process.

Hypnotic methods for exploring higher states of awareness include:

- Ultra-Height

- Ultra-Depth

- Profound Somnambulism

- Simpson Protocol

- Past Life Regression

Attempts to enter into higher states *before* releasing the internal blocks seldom yield more than a recreational trip. Until the client is able to integrate spiritual resources into daily life, higher states tend to be *special* and self-serving. This is what the older daughter represents.

The younger daughter, however, signifies a more enlightened state. Her willingness to please is not based on the vulnerability or survival needs of a child. This is a conscious decision to commit to the future while honoring the past – both the old king and the future king. To please means to make happy. The original meaning of the word happy was equal. Authentic power is not better-than or less-than. It's equal. Happy. Whole and complete.

To heal is to make happy. – **A Course in Miracles**

Integration

A big wedding followed. And thus, the devil's grimy brother got the king's daughter. And when the old king died, Hans became king over the whole country.

In myths and fairy tales, marriage signifies integration. Mind and body are now united. Head and heart are now aligned. Thinking and feeling are now congruent. Conscious and Subconscious Mind are now in accord. The client is now destined to live into the promise of their vision for themselves – their Future Self.

In ancient mythology, the king was wedded to the land, signifying a position of responsibility, being in service to a power greater than oneself. Kingship does not mean controlling *out there*. An *out there* doesn't exist. Only our perception of the world exists. Self-rulership means taking responsibility for all that you see.

The client has seen how it was for them, as a Child. They have seen their life story, how their experiences shaped his identity, and they have learned from this. They have gone through the helplessness and dependency of childhood and grown themselves up. As a result, they have set themselves free to be themself. Because the client now realizes that they are not their mother or father, their fate is their own. This self-awareness will determine how they will live from now on.

Fear of rejection, fear of criticism, fear of being denied what the client wants puts them back in the high-chair, at the mercy of Mommy and Daddy. But kings do not please to get their needs met. Good kings' rule with strength and wisdom. Kings serve a higher calling in life. A person who has a sense of mission in life lives in a state of integrity where the self is aligned with Self, and Self-will is in service to a Higher Power. This is true kingship.

No longer bound to the past, the client is now free to serve a purpose greater than themselves. Having healed the wounds of the past, they are now psychologically prepared to explore higher states of consciousness. If they so wish, they are now free to discover inner sources of guidance, purpose, talents, and abilities yet to be revealed to them.

You hold in your hands a map to buried treasure! What you must do now is hone your ability to recognize when X marks the spot. What happens next is up to you. But know this . . . all the hard-work of navigating the territory of the Subconscious Mind will reward your clients in unexpected ways. You may even surprise yourself as you discover how these simple strategies yield remarkable results! You have all the information you need. Just keep it simple, follow the logical path, and you will succeed. — **Wendie Webber**

CHAPTER 22:
It's All Story

I read somewhere that the universe is made up of stories. Since the dawn of time, stories have been used to both entertain and preserve cultural history and traditions. An oral tradition preceded written accounts, and many societies developed symbolic memory systems to preserve their stories for future generations. Two examples are the Kabbalist Tree of Life and the Native American Medicine Wheel.

In the days of old, the wandering bards and minstrels acted as traveling news reporters. The songs and folk tales they delivered were stories about distant places and historical events. Folk and fairy tales have continued to be enjoyed down through the ages and become associated with children's bedtime stories. Unlike our modern-day Disney variations, however, fairy tales were not all light and goodness. Some could be downright bloody! This is because the purpose of folk tales was to prepare a human soul for the grim realities of life on earth.

Many fairy tales do not end well because, in real life, happily-ever-after is only one potential outcome. Real life can be difficult. It's often unfair. Lessons can be hard-earned. And not everybody gets to retire to a life of leisure aboard their yacht at age 55.

Every problem a client brings you comes wrapped in a Story. The client's presenting issue may be physical, mental, or emotional, but symptoms are never the whole Story. The rest of the Story is hidden beneath the surface of consciousness in the part of the Mind that is responsible for all our memories and emotions. Every unwanted thought, feeling, or behavior is coming out of the client's personal history. So, that's where we must go to find the solution to the problem.

Negative experiences growing up can have a lasting effect by generating unwanted symptoms – physically, mentally, or emotionally. But the problem is not about what happened in a past event. It's the client's interpretation of what was *happening* at the time that's at the root of the problem. This is the client's Pain Story.

The Pain Story

What makes the Mind a living hell is the client's Pain Story. It is the *tale of woe* the client has been telling themselves, over and over again, in the privacy of their own Mind. This Story may have its roots in an actual life experience, but when you regress your client back to the ISE, their Subconscious Mind is not showing you a factual event. It is showing you the perceptions, thoughts, and feelings, and reactions that were shaped by that experience at the age the memory was formed.

Memory is not a recording of truth or fact. It's a recording of perceptions, thoughts, feelings, and responses that made an impression on the client, often at an early age. The Subconscious Mind is the Emotional Mind. So, what makes any event memorable – real or imagined – has to do with the emotions connected with it. If there's an emotional charge still attached to a past event, as far as the Subconscious Mind is concerned, that's a very real and present concern. As a result, left unchallenged, a fearful thought will continue to generate negative emotion at a Subconscious level of Mind.

Emotions are meant to stir us to take action to meet important needs. For every unwanted behavior or reaction, there's an uncomfortable emotion driving it. What's causing that emotion is a thought. A thought is a decision of Mind that, when sufficiently reinforced, becomes a belief. A belief is a Subconscious Truth that determines how we view ourselves and the world of people and things around us. It's all based on a Story.

This is all that you are changing through the process of regression to cause hypnosis – the client's Story. The Story is about how the client interpreted an experience. This is based on the emotional maturity of the client at that time. As a result, if something happened at the age of two to cause the client distress, there's a good chance a two-year-old is still running some part of their life.

Memories of experiences growing up are really just impressions that got stored in memory as *if* they were true. They're based on the consciousness present at the age the event occurred. If something *actually* happened, you can't change that. Nor should you try. What you can do is help the client to come to terms with their past. You do this by changing how they interpret the experiences. You do this by finding some good in the experience.

Every past experience has value when viewed through the lens of Adult Consciousness. With Wisdom, each painful chapter in the Story can be transformed into a learning experience that can then be used to empower the client and support the development of the Soul.

Alchemy

This process of transforming consciousness for the better, real or imagined, is called alchemy. Alchemy is the process through which the philosophers of old sought to discover the elixir of immortality through the process of transmuting base metals (lead) into gold. The name alchemy reflects this theme of transmutation, e.g., *Alkamye* from the Old French, from Medieval Latin, Arabic *Al kimiya* (meaning the transmutation), and the Late Greek *khemeia* (meaning the art of transmutation).

Alchemy is a form of ancient chemistry which, some believe, has its roots in ancient Egypt. Egypt was originally known as *Khem*, the Egyptian word for black, referring to the black, fertile soil of the Nile upon which life in ancient Egypt was dependent. But where modern chemistry deals with the empirical realm, alchemy is a spiritual process whose purpose is to reveal the underlying essence of all things.

This underlying essence is often referred to as "the beauty of All Beauty," "the love of All Love," and "the High Most High." This Highest or Divine Order is the goal of alchemy. The ancient Alchemist writings make clear, however, that the substance of transmutation was not literally lead but the human soul.

Alchemy could be called the Transmutation of Perception. It is a process of changing one's perception by transmuting the ordinary, lead-like, material level of perception to the level of perceiving the gold-like perfection of the highest order in everything, in other words, seeing the Divine in everything. This is the gold of the heart.

Alchemy pertains to the hidden reality of the highest order, which constitutes the underlying essence of all truths and all religions. –
Stanislas Klossowski de Rola

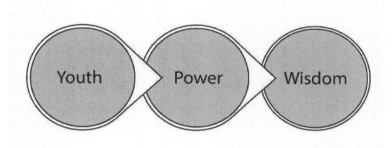

Soul's Journey

From a spiritual perspective, human development is a vehicle for the Soul's Journey through time and space. Just as a caterpillar is transformed through the cocoon stage to emerge as a butterfly, the human Soul undergoes three distinct stages of development –the Youth, Power, and Wisdom Cycles.

Frederick Nietzsche described these successive stages of development in his story about the Camel, Lion, and Child. The Camel says, "Put a load on me." Once loaded, he is sent out into the desert to face the dragon. Every scale on the dragon bears the words Thou Shalt. The Camel's task is to confront and defeat this dragon. To accomplish this, the Camel must be transformed into a Lion. When the Lion emerges victorious from this challenge, he is transformed into a Child.

Become as little children. –**Matthew 18:3 (KJV)**

The Youth Cycle

In the journey of the Soul through life, the Camel represents the Youth Cycle. The purpose of the Youth Cycle is to develop a sense of identity and a way of being in the world that supports physical survival. This is the stage in human development where we learn how to make our way in the world as a physical being.

Camels are beasts of burden. Like a camel, a child takes on the burden of encultured beliefs by accepting familial and societal values. The Child says, "Teach me," and accepts, uncritically, the beliefs and opinions of those in authority.

A camel is able to travel long distances in the desert because it carries the water it needs within. So, it is with the human Soul. What sustains each of us, in the desert of rational, domesticated thinking, is our emotional nature.

The Power Cycle

The Lion, an ancient solar emblem signifying divinity and nobility, represents the Power Cycle. The process of being transformed into a Lion is about finding one's inner strength and rebelling against external values. We must face our fears of rejection, abandonment, the opinion of others, and, sometimes, even death, to come into our authentic power.

The Power Cycle is designed to prepare us for our purpose in life. This cycle is frequently initiated by some sort of a crisis which serves to break us out of encultured thinking. This crisis might come as a divorce, serious illness, accident, loss of a loved one, one's career, etc. but such an event is meant to remind us that we're made of sterner stuff than flesh and bone. By challenging our beliefs, we reclaim our

Core Integrity. This is what allows a person to live from a place of authentic power while accepting Life on its own terms.

The Wisdom Cycle

Nietzsche's Child represents the Wisdom Cycle because it is by living in alignment with our authentic nature that true happiness is realized. Because no Soul is better-than or less-than any other Soul, Wisdom allows you to accept others as they are. This is how you become your *own king*.

Wisdom is expressing your Core Integrity by living authentically and creatively, in service to that which holds heart and meaning for us. Following the Power Cycle, we turn back to the world to share our gifts, knowledge, and experience for the betterment of humanity.

This concept is reflected in the Native American oral tradition of the Medicine Wheel, which recognizes that, when a society has no written records, old people matter. An elder is considered a living repository of tribal history. As such, they bear a responsibility to pass on what they know for the benefit of the tribe and future generations.

The responsibility granted by the Wisdom Cycle is to give in a way that is so authentic that it makes the heart sing. Authentic teaching is not words but a demonstration. It's living your Truth. Sai Baba said it this way, "My life is my teaching."

Soul's Journey is a Wisdom Story. It serves to teach. The Old Testament stories about Moses and Joseph follow the three cycles of Soul's Journey. Wisdom stories abound in every culture in the form of folk tales, parables, and myth. A myth is not a historical accounting of an event. It is a story that is true on the inside, not on the outside, as is memory.

Know thyself and you will know the universe. - **Socrates**

The Devil's Therapy

The Devil's Grimy Brother is a Wisdom Story. Hidden within it are the secrets to transforming human consciousness for the better. The Story begins in the Youth Cycle, which loads each of us up with emotional baggage. Nobody escapes this. We have all been conditioned to assume a false identity – Victim to External Conditions.

To survive, we had to be tough little soldiers. We learned to suck it up and soldier on by repressing our feelings and relying primarily on thinking. The problem is that our best thinking is powerless against the truth of our emotions. This internal conflict is at the root of every problem we experience in life.

The conflicts of the Youth Cycle set us up for a journey that challenges us to reclaim our authentic power by healing the wounds of the past. The Power Cycle is the healing cycle that brings us into the emotional realm of Soul Consciousness. This is the devil's domain, the territory of the Subconscious Mind, where we are required to do the work of self-change.

To heal, we must be prepared to confront the unresolved memories and emotions of the past. The problem is that keeping the lid on the past has made the Subconscious Mind a living hell. And to *go there* requires a deal with the devil. Left unresolved, these painful thoughts and emotional energies from the past will continue to bubble and boil, generating symptoms. So, if there's no other way . . .

The Fisher King is a person who never makes the deal with the devil. He never becomes his *own king* because he is not willing to do the work of self-healing. He is the epitome of the passive patient. Rather than face the wounds of his past, he seeks outer solutions, fishing in the moat surrounding the castle. Every day a new pill comes on the market, a new diet, a new patch, a new therapy promising magical powers. Meanwhile, the solution is offered daily, by analogy, in the sickness itself.

Unfortunately, social conditioning has established a mechanistic world view where broken people need to be fixed. The problem is that the medical model science has given us reflects a mind-body split that doesn't actually exist. Behavior modification, drug therapy, and surgical interventions cannot heal a sickness of the soul. At best, they offer only temporary relief.

Ancient cultures did not have a separatist view of the universe. Science and religion were one. The healer was both a priest and a physician. When formulating a treatment strategy, mind, body, and spirit were considered equally. While new sciences are emerging to challenge the old mechanistic, materialistic world-view, the Universe is still viewed primarily as a big machine made up of separate parts, all working independently.

When machines break down, they need to be fixed. This approach actually works when it comes to repairing lacerations, torn ligaments, or broken bones. But when it comes to treating chronic physical or emotional complaints, the body-as-machine approach fails us miserably. The Guy in the Woods knows better. He recognizes that Mind and body do not function independently, and the body cannot make decisions.

Decision-making is a function of the Mind! The devil knows that the Subconscious Mind is the body-Mind and that the body doesn't lie. He knows this because he is Pan, the God of Nature. The Devil's Therapy works with Nature because Nature heals.

You can't *make* a person heal. Nobody can. The power to heal is in the Mind of the client. To heal, the client must be willing to allow healing to happen. That can take time. While healing *can* happen in an instant, most of the time, what's required is a process of accruing enough *sweepings* to shift the balance. For this reason, the Devil's Therapy is not a quick-fix solution; it's a client-centered solution.

The Devil's Therapy is not a passive process; it demands effort on the part of the client. This is because it takes consciousness to heal consciousness. That's what we're healing. True healing is not about getting rid of the symptoms. It's about releasing the blocks to allowing healing to happen because, if the cause of all sickness is within, so too is the cure.

Emotional healing isn't just first aid. Seemingly minor scrapes in childhood are traumatic to the Child who had to endure them alone. In the Child's mind, he has taken a bullet. When no one is present to soothe the Child and dress the wound, the bullet stays lodged painfully within. Over time it can fester, leading to compulsive behaviors, addiction, and physical dis-ease later in life.

Emotional healing is about finding and removing the bullet. While this can be delicate work, especially when the bullet is lodged painfully close to the heart, The Devil's Therapy offers a solution by giving you the keys to effective regression to cause therapeutic hypnosis.

Your task is not to seek for love, but merely to seek and find all the barriers within yourself that you have built against it. — **Rumi**

Phase 1: Set-Up			Phase 2: Transform		Phase 3: Verify	
1 Intake	2 Educate	3 Test	4 Regression to Cause (R2C)	5 Inner Child Work	6 Testing	7 Forgiveness Work
Establish Therapeutic Relationship	Establish Therapeutic Contract	Test & Prepare for R2C	Locate the Underlying Cause	Re-Story	Test & Integrate Changes	Effortless Permanence
#1 Preliminary Uncovering	#1 Hypnosis Agreement	#1 Hypnosis Tests	#1 Find a Bridge	#1 Dialogue Work	#1 Test the ISE	#1 Restore Goodness
#2 Identify Symptom Resolution Keys	#2 Regression Agreement	#2 Regression Tests	#2 Test for ISE	#2 Re-Parent the Child	#2 Test the SSEs & Compound Change	#2 Release the Grievance
		#3 Teach Universal Healing	#3 Uncover the Story	#3 Re-Story the ISE	#3 Test in Real Life	#3 Forgiveness Test
						#4 Reclaim Wholeness
						#5 Age Progression

You can download a free Infographic of the complete system at www.devilstherapy.com

A Complete System

The Devil's Therapy is comprised of a three-phase, seven-step protocol that will transform your hypnosis sessions into healing programs that deliver real and lasting results — consistently. The three phases of the system act as scaffolding for the seven-step protocol. Together, they give you a step-by-step guide to facilitating the healing process of regression to cause hypnosis.

If you like what you've learned so far, please take a moment to write me a review. Your feedback helps others to decide whether this book might be right for them.

If you are a teacher of Regression to Cause hypnosis, this book can help to empower your students in their sessions with clients. As they gain experience, it will help to deepen their understanding of the healing process. As they shine in the work they do with clients, that light will reflect back upon you.

Phase 1: Set-Up

The first phase in the system focuses on setting up for successful Regression to Cause hypnotherapy. This is comprised of the first three steps in the therapeutic process:

1. The Intake Process
2. The Educational Pre-Talk
3. The Ready for Regression Session

The Intake Process supports you in establishing a Therapeutic Relationship with both the Conscious and Subconscious Mind of the client. It also provides you with the information you need to guide the healing process by allowing you to identify symptom patterns.

The Educational Pre-Talk prepares the client to be an active participant in his own healing by making him a partner in the therapeutic process of regression to cause hypnosis.

The first hypnosis session then acts as a test to ensure that you have a binding Contract while teaching the client how to do the work of self-healing. This lays the foundation for effective regression hypnotherapy.

Get the Complete First Session System here: www.tribeofhealers.com/ready-for-regression-first-session-system-course

Phase 2: Transform

Nothing will change until the client is willing to face the uncomfortable Story that they've been telling themself, about themself, in the privacy of their own Mind. Phase 2 is where causal experience is located and transformed through the next two steps:

4.   Regression to Cause (R2C)
5.   Inner Child Work

The two Rs in R2C stand for Regress and Release. Regression uses Bridging Methods and testing to locate the Initial Sensitizing Event (ISE) and uncover the emotional Story formed by that experience.

Releasing reveals the Parts that got trapped in the event. Inner Child Work includes Dialogue Work, Re-Parenting, and Re-Storying to transform the perceptions, thoughts, and feelings associated with the causal event and allow healing.

Learn the Root Cause Remedy for Results here: www.tribeofhealers.com/root-cause-remedy-for-results-course

Phase 3: Verify

The goal of regression hypnotherapy is not merely improvement. It is effortless permanence, emotional non-reactivity, and permanent symptom cessation. Phase 3 focuses on reinforcing all changes and testing to ensure that the work of healing is complete. This involves two final steps of the seven-step therapeutic process:

6. Testing & Integrating
7. Forgiveness Work

Testing is important at every stage of the healing process, but in Phase 3, it is an extension of the Re-Storying aspect of Inner Child Work. This involves testing at the ISE to verify that the event is clear before growing the Child up. Testing each SSE as you grow the Child up allows you to identify and unresolved aspects and generalize all changes.

Regression hypnotherapy is not a single session approach because the only way to know if the results will last is to test them in the client's daily life. That's where post-hypnotic suggestions take effect. The most important test of the results is the time between sessions.

The process of growing the Child up prepares the client for the Forgiveness Work by restoring to the client his innate goodness and worth. Forgiveness is the final step in the healing process because facing and forgiving the people who hurt us requires Adult Consciousness. Releasing any grievances towards these people will set the client free of their influence.

When forgiveness is complete, the client can reclaim their right to choose their own path from now on. Age Progression then gives you a way to test the client's expectations for the future while reinforcing a realistic identity that is aligned with the client's goals and wishes.

So, that's it.

It's up to you now. Your task, now, is to implement what you have learned. Coach Trainer Hilton Johnson said that in anything you choose to do, you will only be as good as the amount of study, practice, and implementation you put into it.

If you take the time to practice and review what you've learned, you'll become more consistent in your approach to healing. Being consistent will get you more consistent results. Just follow the steps, and you'll get there easily. As you grow your skill and confidence, you'll grow your reputation for delivering results that last.

That's how you'll grow a referral-based healing practice!

Ready to learn more?

Join the Tribe to receive weekly updates at www.tribeofhealers.com and get access to this awesome free course! **The Hypnosis Practice Business System Course** gives you an overview of how to grow a referral-based regression hypnotherapy practice in five simple steps.

You'll find a list of **recommended books and resources** here: www.tribeofhealers.com/wendie-recommends

On Facebook? Join the **Regression Hypnotherapy group**. That's where I hang out! www.facebook.com/groups/32039528511828

Got questions? Post to the group or send me an email! I will reply. wendie@tribeofhealers.com

Recommended Reading

Ashleigh Brilliant wrote: "My life has been greatly influenced by many books I have never read." How true! The following list is, by no means, comprehensive. But I have read them!

Counseling Skills

Dass, Ram & Gorman, Paul. *How Can I Help?* Knopf Publishing.

Kaufman, Barry Neil. *To Love is to be Happy With.* Fawcett Books.

McKay, Matthew. Davis, Martha. Fanning, Patrick. *Messages; The Communication Skills Book.* New Harbinger Publications.

Small, Jacquelyn. *Becoming Naturally Therapeutic; A Return to the True Essence of Helping.* Bantam Books.

Dream Work & Imagery

Arrien, Angeles. *Signs of Life; Five Universal Shapes and How to Use Them.* Arcus Publishing Co.

Barth, Diane. *Daydreaming.* Viking Press.

Born, Margot. *Seven Ways to Look at A Dream.* Starhill Press.

Churchill, Randal. *Become the Dream; The Transforming Power of Hypnotic Dreamwork.* Transforming Press.

Day, Laura. *Practical Intuition*. Villard Publishing.

Delaney, Gayle. *Sensual Dreaming*. Fawcett Publications.

Delaney, Gayle. *Living Your Dreams*. Harper Collins.

Delaney, Gayle. *Breakthrough Dreaming*. Bantam Books.

Ellis, Leslie. *A Clinician's Guide to Dream Therapy: Implementing Simple and Effective Dreamwork*. Routledge.

Faraday, Ann. *The Dream Game*. Harper Collins.

Fezler, William. *Creative Imagery; How to Visualize in All Five Senses*. Fireside Books.

Gendlin, Eugene. *Let Your Body Interpret Your Dreams*. Chiron Publications.

Hoss, Robert J. *Dream Language; Self Understanding through Imagery and Color*.

Johnson, Robert A. *Inner Work*. Harper & Row.

Johnson, Robert. *He*. Harper & Row.

Johnson, Robert. *She*. Harper & Row.

Johnson, Robert. *We*. Harper & Row.

Jung, C.G. *Man & His Symbols*. Doubleday.

King, Serge *Kahili*. *Urban Shaman*. Fireside Books.

Kaplan-Williams, *Stephon. Dreamworking*. Journey Press.

Lusk, Julie T. *30 Scripts for Relaxation Imagery & Inner Healing*. Whole Person Associates.

Mindell, Arnold. *Dreambody; The Body's Role in Revealing the Self*. Sigo Press.

Pearson, Carol S. *The Hero Within: Six Archetypes We Live By*. Harper & Row.

Pike, Diane Kennedy. *Life As A Waking Dream*. Riverbend Books.

Schwartz, Andrew E. *Guided Imagery for Groups*. Whole Person Associates.

Vaughan-Lee, Llewellyn. *The Lover & The Serpent; Dreamwork Within a Sufi Tradition*. Element Books.

Von Franz, Marie-Louse. *The Way of the Dream*. Windrose Films Ltd.

Walker, Matthew. *Why We Sleep; Unlocking the Power of Sleep and* Dreams.

Scribner.

Energy Psychology

Carrington, Patricia. *Try It On Everything; Discover the Power of EFT*. Try It Productions.

Craig, Gary. *EFT for PTSD*. Energy Psychology Press.

Craig, Gary. *EFT for Weight Loss*. Energy Psychology Press.

Feinstein, David. *Energy Psychology Interactive; Self-Help Guide.* Innersource.

Feinstein, David/Eden, Donna/Craig, Gary. *The Promise of Energy Psychology; Revolutionary Tools for Dramatic Personal Change.* Jeremy P. Tarcher/Penguin

Gallo, Fred P. Vincenzi, Harry. *Energy Tapping.* New Harbinger Publications.

Gallo, Fred P. *Energy Tapping for Trauma.* New Harbinger Publications. Gordon, Marilyn. Extraordinary Healing. WiseWord Publishing.

Hawkins, David R. *Power vs. Force;* The Hidden Determinants of Human Behavior. Hay House.

Hartman, Silvia. Oceans of Energy; Patterns & Techniques of EmoTrance™. DragonRising.

Sparks, Loretta. Emotional Freedom Techniques Personal Peace Procedure. Emotions

Abramson, Edward. *Emotional Eating; A Practical Guide to Taking Control.* Lexington Books.

Banyan, Calvin D. *The Secret Language of Feelings.* Abbot Publishing.

Bradshaw, John. *Healing the Shame That Binds You.* Health Communications.

Bradshaw, John. *Homecoming.* Bantam Books.

Borysenko, Joan. *Guilt is the Teacher Love is the Lesson.* Warner Books.

Childre, Doc/ Rozman, Deborah. *Transforming Anger; The HeartMath Solution for Letting Go of Rage, Frustration and Irritation.* New Harbinger Publications.

Ecker, Bruce. Ticic, Robin. Hulley, Laurel. *Unlocking the Emotional Brain: Eliminating Symptoms at Their Roots Using Memory Reconsolidation.* Routledge.

Hicks, Esther and Jerry. *The Astonishing Power of Emotions.* Hay House.

Gray, John. *What You Feel You Can Heal.* Heart Publishing.

Jampolsky, Gerald G. *Love Is Letting Go of Fear.* Bantam Books.

Jenson, Jean. *Reclaiming Your Life.* Dutton Books.

Lowen, Alexander. *Depression & the Body.* Penguin Books.

Luskin, Fred. *Forgive for Good.* HarperCollins.

Miller, Alice. *The Drama of the Gifted Child.* Harper. Needleman, Jacob. A Little Book on Love. Doubleday

Grandin, Temple. *Animals In Translation.* Harcourt.

Tipping, Colin C. *Radical Forgiveness.* Global 13 Publications.

Truman, Karol K. *Feelings Buried Alive Never Die …*

Vanderpol, Johanna. *Honoring Your Emotions; Why it Matters.* Nine Lives Publishing.

Whitfield, Charles L. *A Gift to Myself.* Health Communications.

Wiesenthal, Simon. *The Sunflower; On the Possibilities and Limits of Forgiveness.* Schocken books

Young, Jeffrey/ Klosko, Janet. *Reinventing Your Life.* Plume

Hypnosis & Clinical Hypnotherapy

Banyan, Calvin & Kein, Gerald. *Hypnosis & Hypnotherapy.* Abbot Publishing House, Inc.

Barnett, E.A. *Analytical Hypnotherapy; Principles & Practice.* Westwood Publishing Co.

Battinos, Rubin, *Expectation; The Very Brief Therapy Book.* Crown Publishing.

Boyne, Gil, *Transforming Therapy; A New Approach to Hypnotherapy.* Westwood Publishing Co.

Bristol, Claude M. *The Magic of Believing; The Science of Reaching Your Goal.* Prentice Hall Press.

Churchill, Randal. Regression *Hypnotherapy: Transcripts of Transformation, Vol. 1.* Transforming Press.

Churchill, Randal., *Catharsis in Regression Hypnotherapy: The Regression Therapy Training Guide, Vol 2.* Transforming Press.

Elias, Jack. *Finding True Magic: Transpersonal Hypnotherapy.* Five Wisdoms Publications

Elman, Dave. *Hypnotherapy.* Westwood Publishing Co.

Hammond, D. Corydon. *Handbook of Hypnotic Suggestions & Metaphors.* Norton Publishing.

Hickman, Irene. *Mind Probe-Hypnosis.*

Hilgard, Ernest and Josephine. *Hypnosis in the Relief of Pain.* Routledge

Hogan, Kevin. *The New Hypnotherapy Handbook.* Network 3000 Publishing.

Hogan, Kevin. *Covert Hypnosis.* Network 3000 Publishing.

Hunter, C. Roy. *Art of Hypnosis.* Kendall/Hunt Publishing Co.

Hunter, C. Roy. *Art of Hypnotherapy.* Kendall/Hunt Publishing Co.

Kappas, John G. *Professional Hypnotism Manual.* Panorama Publishing Co.

Kappas, John G., *Relationship Strategies; The E & P Attraction.* Panorama Publishing Co.

King, Mark E., Citrenbaum, Charles M. *Existential Hypnotherapy.* Guilford Press

Lecron, Leslie & Bordeaux, Jean. *Hypnotism Today.* Wilshire Book Co.

Murphy, Joseph. *The Power of Your Subconscious* Mind. Bantam Books.

McGill, Ormond. *Professional Stage Hypnotism.* Westwood Publishing Co.

Quigley, David. *Alchemical Hypnotherapy.* Alchemy Institute of Healing Arts

Rosen, Sidney. *My Voice Will Go With You; The Teaching Tales of Milton H. Erickson.* Norton & Co.

Williams, John K. *Wisdom of Your Subconscious Mind.* Prentice Hall, Inc.

Winkler, E. Arthur Winkler, *Hypnotherapy*

Rosenthal, Allen M. *Your Mind The Magician.* DeVorss & Co.

Life Purpose/Mission & Self Mastery

Bogart, Greg. *Finding Your Life's Calling.* Dawn Mountain Press.

Cameron, Julia. *The Artist's Way; A Spiritual Path to Higher Creativity.* Tarcher/Putnam Books.

Covey, Stephen R. *The 7 Habits of Highly Effective People.* Fireside Books.

Csikszentmihalyi, Mihaly. *Flow; the Psychology of Optimal Experience.* Harper Books.

Jarow, Rick. *Creating the Work You Love.* Destiny Books.

Leonard, George. *Mastery: The Keys to Success & Long-Term Fulfillment.* Dutton Books.

Millman, Dan. *The Life You Were Born to Live.* H.J. Kramer Ltd.

Moore, Thomas. *Care of the Soul.* Harper Books.

Needleman, Jacob. *Money & the Meaning of Life.* Doubleday.

Nemeth, Maria. *The Energy of Money.* Ballantine Wellspring.

Sher, Barbara. *I Could Do Anything* (If I Only Knew What It Was). Delacorte Press.

Spangler, David. *The Call.* Riverhead Books.

Stephan, Naomi. *Finding Your Life Mission.* Stillpoint Publishing.

Mind-Body Healing

Achterberg, Jeanne. Dossey, Barbara. Kokmeier, Leslie. *Rituals of Healing; Using Imagery for Health & Wellness.* Bantam New Age Books.

Bays, Brandon. *The Journey; A Road Map to the Soul.* Pocket Books.

Chopra, Deepak. *Quantum Healing.* Bantam New Age Books.

Coddington, Mary. *In Search of The Healing Energy.* Destiny Books.

Davidsson, Marcy Foley/Shaffer, William L./Davidsson, Kent. *Illuminating Physical Experience.* Holistic Wellness Foundation

Dethlefsen, Thorwald. *The Healing Power of Illness; The Meaning of Symptoms & How to Interpret Them.* Element Books.

Dossey, Larry. *Reinventing Medicine.* Harper Books.

Duff, Kat. *The Alchemy of Illness.* Harmony Books.

Epstein, Gerald. *Healing Visualizations; Creating Health Through Imagery.* Bantam Books.

Goldberg, Bruce. *Soul Healing.* Llewellyn Books.

Goldberg, Bruce. *Secrets of Self-Hypnosis.* Sterling Publishing Co., Inc.

Greenwood, Michael & Nunn, Peter. *Paradox & Healing*. Meridian House.

Hamer, Ryke Geerd. *Scientific Chart of Germanic New Medicine*.

Hay, Louise L. *You Can Heal Your Life*. Hay House Publishing.

Hay, Louise L. *Heal Your Body*. Hay House Publishing.

Helmstetter, Shad. *What to Say When You Talk to Your Self*. Pocket Books.

LeShan, Lawrence. *Cancer As A Turning Point*. Penguin Books.

Liebmann-Smih, Joan, Egan, Jacqueline Nardi. *Body Signs*. Bantam Books.

Lipton, Bruce H. *The Biology of Belief*. Hay House.

Locke, Steven. Colligan, Douglas. *The Healer Within*. Dutton Books.

McTaggart, Lynne. *The Field*. Free Press

McTaggart, Lynne. *The Intention Experiment*. Free Press.

Moss, Richard. *The Black Butterfly; An Invitation to Radical Aliveness*. Celestial Arts.

Myss, Caroline. *Anatomy of the Spirit*. Harmony Books.

Myss, Caroline. *Why People Don't Heal & How They Can*. Harmony Books.

Parkhill, Stephen. *Answer Cancer*. Omni Hypnosis Publishing.

Rubin, Theodore Isaac. *The Angry Book*. Collier Books.

Rocha, Cairo P. *Anger goes up, Fear goes down – Emotions and the Hidden Link*. Authorhouse

Rossi, Ernest L., *Cheek, David B. Mind-Body Therapy; Methods of Ideodynamic Healing in Hypnosis*. Norton & Co.

Sarno, John E. *The Mindbody Prescription*. Warner Books.

Sarno, John E. *The Divided Mind; Epidemic of Mindbody Disorders*. Harper Collins

Siegel, Bernie. *Love, Medicine & Miracles*. Harper & Row.

Silva, Jose. *Silva Mind Control Method for Getting Help from Your Other Side*. Pocket Books.

Sopher, Marc. *To Be or Not To Be … Pain Free; The Mindbody Syndrome*.

Taylor, Jill Bolte. *My Stoke of Insight; A Brain Scientist's Personal Journey*. Viking

Tebbetts, *Charles. Self Hypnosis & Other Mind-Expanding Techniques*. Westwood Publishing Co. Inc.

Walker, Morton. *The Power of Color*. Avery Publishing.

Weissman, Darren R. *The Power of Infinite Love & Gratitude; An Evolutionary Journey to Awakening Your Spirit*. Hay House.

Neurolinguistic Programming (NLP)

Andreas, Connirae. Andreas, Tamara. *Core Transformation; Reaching the Wellspring Within*. Real People Press.

Andreas, Steve & Connirae. *Change Your Mind.* Real People Press.

Bandler, Richard & Grinder, John. *Frogs Into Princes.* Real People Press.

Bandler, Richard & Grinder, John. *Reframing.* Real People Press.

Grinder, John & Bandler, Richard, *Trance-Formations.* Real People Press.

Linden, Anne. *Mindworks.* Berkley Books.

Robbins, Anthony. *Unlimited Power.* Fawcett Press.

Parts Therapy

Emmerson, Gordon. *Ego State Therapy.* Crown House Publishing

Harris, Thomas A. *I'm OK – You're OK; A Practical Guide to Transactional Analysis.* Harper and Row Publishers

Hunter, C. Roy. *Hypnosis for Inner Conflict Resolution; Introducing Parts Therapy.* Crown House Publishing Ltd.

Napier, Nancy J. *Recreating Your Self; Building Self-Esteem through Imaging and Self-Hypnosis.* W.W. Norton

Parks, Penny. *The Counselors Guide to Parks Inner Child Therapy.* Human Horizons Series.

Pierrakos, Eva. *The Pathwork of Self-Transformation.* Bantam Books

Pierrakos, Eva. *Surrender to God Within; Pathwork at the Soul Level.* Pathwork Press

Satir, Virginia. *The Satir Model; Family Therapy and Beyond.* Science & Behavior Books.

Schmidt, Shirley Jean. *The Developmental Needs Meeting Strategy: An Ego State Therapy for Healing Adults with Childhood Trauma and Attachment Wounds.* DNMS Institute.

Stone, Hal and Sidra. *Embracing Our Selves; The Voice Dialogue Manual.* Nataraj Publishing

Unterman, Debbie. *Talking to My Selves; Learning to Love the Voices in Your Head.*

Watkins, John and Helen. *Ego States; Theory and Therapy.* W.W. Norton Whitfield, Charles L. Healing the Child Within. Health Communications.

Zimberoff, Diane. *Breaking Free from the Victim Trap.* Wellness Press.

Zinker, Joseph. *Creative Process in Gestalt Therapy.*

Regression Therapy

Chadwick, Gloria. *Discovering Your Past Lives.* Contemporary Books.

Dethlefsen, Thorwald. *Challenge of Fate.* Element Books Ltd.

Dethlefsen, Thorwald. *Voices from Other Lives.* Evans & Co.

Grof, Stanislav. *Holotropic Mind.* Harper Collins.

Haich, Elizabeth. *Initiation.*

Lee, John. Growing *Yourself Back Up: Understanding Emotional Regression.* Harmony

Lucas, Winafred Blake. *Regression Therapy; A Handbook for Professionals.* Deep Forest Press.

Moody, Raymond A. *Life After Life.* Bantam Books.

Newton, Michael. *Journey of Souls.* Llewellyn Publications.

Snow, Chet. *Mass Dreams of the Future.* Deep Forest Press.

Stephens, Elaine. *Whispers of the Mind.* Harper & Row.

Weiss, Brian. *Many Lives, Many Masters.* Fireside Books.

Weiss, Brian. *From Time Into Healing.* Fireside Books.

Spiritual

Amen, Daniel G. Healing the Hardware of the Soul. The Free Press

Atwater, P.M.H. *Beyond the Light; The Mysteries and Revelations of Near Death Experiences.* Avon Books.

Baldwin, William. *Spirit Releasement Therapy; A Technique Manual.* Headline Books.

Fiore, Edith. *The Unquiet Dead; A Psychologist Treats Spirit Possession.* Ballantine Books.

Foundation for Inner Peace, *A Course in Miracles.*

Goldberg, Bruce. Peaceful Transition; *The Art of Conscious Dying & Liberation of the Soul.* Llewellyn Publications.

Goldberg, Bruce. *Soul Healing.* Llewellyn Publications.

Harner, Michael. *The Way of the Shaman.* HarperSanFrancisco

Ingerman, Sandra. *Soul Retrieval; Mending the Fragmented Self.* HarperSanFrancisco

Lazaris. *The Sacred Journey: You and Your Higher Self.* Concept Synergy Publishing.

Kason, Yvonne. A *Farther Shore.* Harper Collins.

Matthews, Caitlin. *Singing the Soul Back Home; Shamanism in Daily Life.* Element Books.

Modi, Shakuntala. *Remarkable Healings.* Hampton Roads.

Moody, Raymond. *Life After Life.* Bantam.

Myss, Caroline. *Sacred Contracts.* Harmony Books.

Newton, Michael. Life *Between Lives; Hypnotherapy for Spiritual Regression.* Llewellyn Books.

Newton, Michael. *Journey of Souls; Case Studies of Life Between Lives.* Llewellyn Books.

Nuland, Sherwin B. *How We Die; Reflections on Life's Final Chapter.* First Vintage Books.

Ruiz, Don Miguel. *Four Agreements Wisdom Book.* Amber Allen Publishing.

Stephens, Elaine. *Whispers of the Mind; A Complete Program for Unlocking the Secrets of Your Past Lives.* Harper & Row

Storm, Howard. *My Descent into Death.* Doubleday.

Van Bommel, Harry. *Family Hospice Care.* Saint Elizabeth Health Care Foundation.

Villodo, Alberto. *Mending the Past and Healing the Future with Soul Retrieval.* Hay House.

Vitale, Joe / Len, Ihaleakala Hew. *Zero Limits.* Wiley

Wapnick, Kenneth. *A Talk Given on A Course in Miracles.* Foundation for A Course in Miracles.

Weiss, Brian L. *Many Lives, Many Masters.* Fireside Books.

Woolger, Roger. *Other Lives, Other Selves; A Jungian Psychotherapist Discovers Past Lives.* Bantam New Age.

Woolger, Roger. *Healing Your Past Lives.* Sounds True.

Zukav, Gary. *The Seat of the Soul.* Fireside Books

Stress & Trauma

Baum, Brent. *The Healing Dimensions; Resolving Trauma in Body, Mind and Spirit.* Healing Dimensions

Levine, Peter A. *Waking the Tiger; Healing Trauma.* North Atlantic Books
Rothschild, Babette. The Body Remembers Casebook. Norton

Scaer, Robert C. *The Body Bears the Burden; Trauma, Dissociation, and Disease.* Haworth Medical Press

Scaer, Robert. *The Trauma Spectrum; Hidden Wounds and Human Resiliency.* W.W. Norton.

Talbott, Shawn. *The Cortisol Connection; Why Stress Makes You Fat and Ruins Your Health.* Hunter House.

Other

Bach, Richard. *Running from Safety; An Adventure of the Spirit.*

Bach, Richard. *Hypnotizing Maria; A Story.* Hampton Roads.

Baum, Brent. *Living As Light; The Awakening of Mystical Consciousness.* Healing Dimensions.

Barksdale, L.S. *Building Self-Esteem.* Barksdale Foundation.

Bly, Robert. *Iron John.* Addison Wesley.

Bryan, Mark & Cameron, Julia. *The Money Drunk; 90 Days to Financial Freedom.* Balentine Books.

Csikszentmihalyi, Mihaly. *Creativity.* Harper Collins.

Csikszentmihalyi, Mihaly. *Flow.* Harper Collins.

Csikszentmihalyi, Mihaly. *The Evolving Self: A Psychology for the Third Millennium.* Harper Collins.

Duerk, Judith. *Circle of Stones: Woman's Journey to Herself.* Lura Medic.

Goleman, Daniel. *Emotional Intelligence.* Bantam Books.

Hicks, Jerry & Esther. *Abraham Speaks: A New Beginning 1 & 2.* Abraham Hicks Publishing

Hill, Napoleon. *Think & Grow Rich.*

Hill, Napoleon. *Master Key to Riches.*

Hopkins, Tom. *How to Master the Art of Selling.* Warner Books.

Leidecker, Arthur. *From Scratch and on a Shoestring.*

Maurer, Robert. *The Kaizen Way.* Workman Publishing.

Satir, Virginia. *Peoplemaking.* Science & Behavior Books.

Shanor, Karen Nesbitt. *The Emerging Mind.* Renaissance Books.

Slade, Neil. *The Frontal Lobes Supercharge.* Neil Slade Music and Books.

Walker, Matthew. *Why We Sleep: Unlocking the Power of Sleep and Dreams.* Simon and Schuster.

It's hopeless! Tomorrow there'll be even more books I should have read than there are today. - **Ashleigh Brilliant**

Glossary of Terms

Abreaction: A physical movement or an emotional outburst as a reaction to a suggestion while in the state of hypnosis. Some hypnotic abreactions are spontaneous, and others are created by the hypnotist. Hypnotic abreaction can be used to acquire greater depth, cause revivification, or remove repressed emotions.

Affect Bridge (AB): The technique, developed by John G. Watkins, whereby the client follows a feeling from the present to a past incident.

Age progression (AP): Also known as future pacing, the client projects himself forward into the future. AP can be used to (a) test the client's expected results following hypnotherapeutic processing, (b) mentally rehearse future situations or event to experience successfully accomplishing a task, (c) to create future scenarios for the purpose of resource development, e.g., assertiveness training, (d) to see a desired outcome or the consequences of their current destructive behavior, e.g., High Road, Low Road, (e) compounding success by celebrating success in the future, (f) strategic planning by looking back from the future to see what concrete steps were taken to achieve success.

Age Regression (AR): The process of moving the client back in time from the present to a past incident in order to confront the cause of the presenting problem at its inception.

Anchoring: A neurolinguistic programming term for a natural process by which a conditioned response is formed. A memory, state, or behavior is associated (anchored) to a specific stimulus. Repeated stimuli then reinforce the association. The anchor (i.e., trigger or stimulus) can be physical (e.g., touch or sensation), visual (e.g., the color red), auditory (e.g., vocal tonality), verbal phrases (e.g., a word or phrase one says to oneself), as well as memories or emotional states (e.g., see a snake, feel fear). Also, see Classical Conditioning.

Body Syndrome: A physical manifestation of an emotional trauma. When an emotion is held in or repressed instead of being processed and released, the emotion will express itself as physical discomfort.

Chair Therapy (CT): This technique derives from the *empty chair technique* of Gestalt therapy, developed by Fritz Perls. Through this technique, the client is directed to place another person or part of himself (e.g., thought, feeling, symptom, aspect of a dream, etc.) in a chair across and several feet away from him. The client carries on a conversation by shifting back and forth between the 'other' and himself. This process allows the client to clarify his feelings and reactions to the other person and increase understanding. Understanding can then be used to facilitate forgiveness and behavioral change.

Classical Conditioning: A form of associative learning that was first demonstrated by Ivan Pavlov (1927), who trained dogs to salivate at the sound of a ringing bell. The conditioning process involves pairing a stimulus to a response. Through repetition, the two become associated, and the response becomes automatic (conditioned) (e.g., fear conditioning). Also, see anchoring.

Cognitive Bridge (CB): Rather than following a feeling, the client follows a thought back from the present to a past incident.

Conscious Mind (CM): In Sigmund Freud's psychoanalytic theory of personality, the conscious mind includes everything that is inside of our awareness. This is the aspect of our mental processing that we can think and talk about in a rational way. The conscious mind includes such things as sensations, perceptions, memories, feelings, and fantasies inside our current awareness. Closely allied with the conscious mind is the preconscious, which includes the things that we are not thinking of at the moment but which we can easily draw into conscious awareness.

Convincer: Any method that provides the client with evidence and, therefore, affirms his or her belief or a course of action. E.g., Eye Lock Test, Time Distortion Test, SUDS.

Core Beliefs: Beliefs that are installed prior to the establishment of the Critical Factor (usually before age 5). Example: "I'm unlovable." "I am stupid/ugly/incapable/etc."

Critical Function (CF): AKA Critical Faculty. The semi-permeable barrier that sits between the conscious and subconscious mind acts as a *guardian at the gate* to protect our subconsciously held beliefs. It has the power to accept or reject suggestions. Suggestions that do not match existing programming automatically get rejected.

Deep Memory Process (DMP): A technique developed by Roger Woolger, Ph.D. that combines Jungian analysis, psychodrama, and shamanic healing techniques to release ancestral or karmic issues and to heal physical and emotional problems that are held in the body.

Direct Drive Technique (DDT): A compounding technique. The law of compound suggestion states that once a suggestion has been accepted by the client's subconscious, it becomes easier for additional suggestions to be accepted. With this process, the client repeats a single suggestion out loud with intention and enthusiasm (15 times or more).

Dark Force Entity (DFE): Also referred to as fallen angels, these spiritual parasites attach themselves to humans for their malicious purposes. They are hierarchical, clever, and are on a mission to gain power by destroying the light. They are often afraid of the light. DFEs have within them a spark of light but have been deceived into losing awareness of their true nature. The objective of Spirit Releasement Therapy (SRT) is to help them realize that they, themselves, are trapped so they can be released back to the light.

Direct Suggestion (DS): Also known as authoritarian or paternal, this method was favored by Dave Elman. Suggestions are given in the form of instructions or commands, such as "Relax your eyelids to the point they just won't work." In contrast, indirect suggestion, or permissive/maternal, was the method favored by Milton Erickson. Indirect suggestions give the client the illusion of choice by deciding whether they will carry out the action requested by the hypnotist; for example, "And you might discover that your eyelids are becoming heavier." Another method that gives the illusion of choice is the double bind technique, which can be direct or indirect. For example: "You can relax now, or you can relax later...whatever's best for you." This gives the client the illusion of choice but presupposes that the client will *relax,* regardless of which option he chooses. This method is useful for analytical types who want to maintain control.

Educational Pre-Talk: The process of educating a client in readiness for therapeutic hypnosis.

Ego States: Various aspects of the personality that formed in response to the client's life experiences. Healthy parts form in response to positive, loving, affirming relationships with role models. Wounded parts form in response to traumas, abuse, neglect, rejection, and enmeshing role models. These parts are stuck in the past, where they continue to hold negative feelings and irrational beliefs which affect the client in the present. Also, see Transactional Analysis.

Emotional Freedom Technique (EFT): Also known as *tapping,* the principle behind EFT is that negative emotions can cause disturbances in the body's energy field. EFT theory derives from similar principles behind those of acupuncture. EFT was originated by Gary Craig, who studied TFT with Roger Callahan.

Energy Psychology: A group of meridian-based therapeutic methods that incorporate tapping, rubbing, or touching of acupressure points or chakras with or without the use of suggestions. Modalities include TFT, EFT, TAT, Seemorg Matrix Work, WHEE, and others. Also, see MTT.

Finger Pinch Technique (FPT): The process whereby the rubbing or pinching of two fingers together is anchored to a specific response (e.g., feeling calm and relaxed).

Forgiveness of Others (FOO): The process of setting oneself free of the past by releasing anger, blame, and condemnation toward an offender and finding some good in past transgressions. This serves to empower the forgiver to relinquish victim status and choose to take responsibility for their life and how they feel.

Forgiveness of Self (FOS): The process of releasing anger, blame, and condemnation toward oneself by reframing past failings or transgressions as mistakes.

Future Pacing (FP): A.K.A. Age Progression, the process of guiding the client to imagine experiencing a future situation or event in order to test the results and reinforce change.

Grownup (GU): Adult consciousness of the client which can provide love, information, and guidance to the younger selves.

High Road, Low Road (HRLR): A 5-PATH adaptation of the Crossroads Patter. The client is guided to imagine him or herself standing at a crossroads. The past stretches out behind them, and the future lies before them along two distinct paths, one to the left and one to the right. The 'right' road is designated the High Road, while the road on the left is the Low Road. The client is then invited to travel down the Low Road to instill aversion to continuing their 'bad' behavior by looking at all the future negative consequences of continuing along this path. The client is then brought back to the crossroads to recognize they can still make the choice for change. They are then guided down the High Road to look at all the positive rewards of making this choice. The Crossroads Patter can also be used following successful clearing to allow the client to experience the road they are now on as a result of having made these positive changes (e.g., future pacing).

Ignorant Spirit (IS): A.K.A. Earthbound Spirit, *hungry ghost, or hitchhiker.* According to spirit attachment theory, when a person dies and doesn't cross over into the light, he becomes earthbound and attaches to a living person. When death comes suddenly, the IS may be confused and not realize he is dead. If he is unwilling to let go of his physical existence, he may avoid going into the light at the time of death. He may fear going to hell because of misdeeds during his life. Or, believing that nothing follows death, he may attempt to remain amongst the living. When an IS attaches to someone, it is generally out of ignorance rather than malice. He may become bound to someone with whom he has unfinished business. A grieving loved one may draw the IS to become attached to them in an attempt to comfort them. Substance abusers may attach to living users in an attempt to feed their addiction (hungry ghosts). A child may seek companionship with another child so as not to be alone.

Initial Sensitizing Event (ISE): Also known as *the seed-planting event or causal event.* The first event which generated the perceptions underlying the client's presenting issue usually occurring in childhood. The event is rarely known to the Conscious Mind. This event, while having an emotional impact at the time, may or may not have been traumatic. Each subsequent event, which in some way resembles the first time, then serves to re-stimulate the pattern established in the ISE, adding to its strength. Reframing the ISE will change the perceptions underlying the problem, allowing a relieving of symptoms.

Inner Child (IC): The client at a younger age. Also referred to as the Little One or Child.

Intake Process: The preliminary interview in which a history of the client's presenting issue is taken.

Mental Rehearsal: the process of imagining or mentally practicing performing a task as opposed to actual practice.

Meridians: Biological energy lines in the body identified by Chinese

Medicine thousands of years ago. Along these lines are sensitive points (acupuncture points) that can be stimulated to release blocks and stimulate the flow of bio-energies in the body for the purposes of healing.

Meridian Tapping Technique (MTT): MTT is the umbrella term for all techniques that utilize acupressure points to reduce or resolve negative emotions and the physical issues associated with them. Tapping practitioners use MTT to release blocks to the body's natural energy flow. Releasing the blocks allows the energy system to rebalance in the body-mind. Acupressure points are located where the meridian pathways are nearer to the skin's surface. Meridian tapping techniques address the energy system in the body by tapping or touching a number of these meridian points. MTT methods include Thought Field Therapy (TFT), Emotional Freedom Technique (EFT), Touch and Breath (TAB), Be Set Free Fast (BSFF), Thought Energy Synchronization Therapy (TEST), Negative Affect Erasing Method (NAEM), Individualized Energy Psychotherapy (IEP), Matrix Re-Imprinting, and others.

Muscle Response Test (MRT): A.K.A. muscle testing or kinesiology. A group of methods used to elicit unconscious (ideomotor) responses through the body. Developed by Dr. George Goodheart as a way to correct structural imbalances, MRT is used to retrieve information from the Subconscious through yes/no or true/false statements. There are various methods that include the Sway Test, the Basic Arm Test, Hand Solo Method, Falling Log Method, Hole-In-One Method, and Linked Rings Method. MRT is used in the classic approach to EFT. Dr. David Hawkins utilized MRT to calibrate emotional energies. He writes about this in his book, Power Vs. Force.

Parts: See Ego States. The primary Parts worked with in regression hypnotherapy sessions are the Inner Child, Adult Part, Parent Parts, and Offender.

Parts Therapy (PT): A.K.A. Ego State Therapy, Subpersonality Work, Parts Mediation Therapy. This method has its roots in Gestalt Therapy. Conflicting parts are identified and then communicated with to bring about a resolution. Parts Therapy was pioneered by Charles Tebbetts. His work is carried on today by C. Roy Hunter.

Past Life Regression (PLR): Regression to an event in a previous incarnation. The belief in past lives is common to many spiritual systems, including early Christianity, which believe in the eternal nature of the soul, which reincarnates. The Yoga Sutras of Patanjali discuss the concept of karma. Karma is essentially the concept of free will; humans have free will to choose good or evil and then experience the consequences of their choices. The soul is believed to be burdened with an accumulation of impressions that are carried over from previous lives.

Progressive Relaxation (PR): Progressive Relaxation generally applies to a relaxation induction. The client is instructed to focus inside the body and, starting at either the top of the head or the feet, imagine relaxing various muscles in a sequential manner. Originally known as Progressive muscle relaxation (PMR), this technique was developed by Edmund Jacobson in the early 1920s as a means of relieving anxiety. Jacobson believed that since muscle tension accompanies anxiety, one can reduce anxiety by relaxing the muscular tension. By sequentially tensing and relaxing muscles in the legs, abdomen, chest, arms, and face, anxiety is, therefore, systematically reduced. Jacobson discovered that this technique is also effective with ulcers, insomnia, and hypertension.

Set-up Statement: A precise statement used to focus the mind on the thoughts, feelings, and memories associated with an issue prior to a round of releasing.

Somatic Bridge: Rather than following a feeling or a thought, the client focuses on a physical sensation and follows it back from the present to a past incident.

Somnambulism: Considered a *working depth* of hypnosis for regression work. This level is easy to test for and provides a very clear and measurable result. Tests include Numbers Challenge (losing the numbers), Eye Fractionation Test, Pinch Test for analgesia, hallucination through suggestion.

Spirit Releasement Therapy (SRT): Sometimes referred to as "a clinical approach to de-possession," SRT was developed by the late Dr. William Baldwin and is covered, in-depth, in his book Spirit Releasement Therapy.

Subconscious Mind (SCM/SM): A.K.A. the Feeling Mind. The part of the mind that is below the threshold of consciousness. The SCM is responsible for feelings, intuition, imagination and holds all the memories. It is the seat of our emotions and is the driving force of our being.

Subjective Unit of Distress Scale (SUDS): Also known as Subjective Units of Disturbance Scale. The client assesses their level of discomfort using an intensity scale; usually, 0 to 10, where 10 is "the worst it has ever been," and 0 is zero distress or "peaceful and comfortable." This self-assessment tool guides the Hypnotherapist while providing the client with convincing evidence of improvement. The SUDS can be used prior to releasing as well as retroactively.

Subsequent Sensitizing Event (SSE): Events subsequent to the ISE, which reinforce the causal event generating a pattern of behavior and/or survival. When life events match the ISE, the pattern of behavior/survival is reinforced, and internal stress increases.

Symptom Producing Event (SPE): The most recently occurring SSE where the underlying problem began to express as symptoms (e.g., the client took up smoking or overeating, the rash appeared, etc.).

Transactional Analysis (TA): Eric Berne's ego states; Parent, Adult, and Child are the three basic parts worked with during regression. TA explains why people respond the way they do to various situations (i.e., behavioral patterns).

Unconscious Mind (UCM): Also known as Body Mind. The deepest stratum of the subconscious mind responsible for automatic body functions such as heart rate, respiration, digestion, elimination, perspiration, etc.

Ultra-Depth (UD): Also known as the Sichort State. To achieve this profound depth of consciousness and awareness, the individual must be conditioned to first achieve profound Somnambulism. The individual must then be conditioned to the Esdaile State (coma state) and be tested by catatonic responses. Finally, the individual must achieve the Sichort State where it is possible to instantly induce either analgesia, local, or general anesthetic suitable for surgery. Regressions in the Sichort State bring forth the actual past personality. In most cases, the subject will have no conscious recall. This is the same state achieved by Edgar Cayce for the purpose of trance channeling. The only level of depth below the Sichort State is natural deep sleep. James Ramey continues the work of Walter Sichort.

Ultra-Height (UH): A method created by Gerald F. Kein which allows the client to reach expanded levels of awareness where he or she can readily obtain knowledge and insight into their physical, mental and/or emotional problems. To achieve this state, the client is first guided into a state of somnambulism. S/he is then guided deeper into the Esdaile State (coma state). Once the Esdaile State is achieved, the client is guided to allow the mind to float free of the body and drift up to increasingly higher planes of consciousness. This heightened state of awareness and mental clarity can be used to identify the root cause of a problem as well as the solution, seek guidance, access knowledge, and achieve healing.

INDEX

A

Abreaction, 93, 343
Abuse, 69, 122, 175, 202, 211, 304, 347, 349
Acceptance, 60, 70, 72, 112, 218-20, 257, 268, 270, 290, 292, 305
Adult, 15, 17, 31, 43, 59, 97. 125, 136, 165-168, 170, 173-79, 193, 194, 199, 202, 203, 208, 209, 211-14, 216, 221, 224, 225, 229, 239, 241, 249, 256, 262, 267-74, 279, 301, 311, 322, 348, 351, 353
Affect Bridge, 143-44, 146, 148, 152. 156. 159, 185, 195, 210, 229, 343
Age Progression, 231, 300, 302, 303, 322, 343, 348
Age Regression, 133, 343
Alchemy, 271, 312, 313
Alzheimer's Disease, 13
Amnesia, 79
Amygdala, 114-15
Animal Magnetism, 9, 11, 12
Anger, 33, 65, 68, 69, 92, 94, 95, 97, 99, 101, 114, 117, 123, 127, 143, 145, 150-56, 159, 169, 181, 185, 187, 189, 190, 191, 201, 215, 220, 234, 235, 262, 269,

272, 274-76, 282-88, 292, 294, 297, 298, 301, 302, 347
Anxiety, 6, 13, 32, 65, 68, 94, 138, 151, 189, 202, 209, 214, 247, 252, 269, 351
Attachment, 211, 274, 275, 348
Auto-Suggestion, 102, 105, 110, 219

B

Benefits of Change, 47, 105, 106, 239, 248, 370, 300
Bridge, 19, 82, 94, 95, 129, 131, 139, 141-44, 146, 155-57, 159-60, 163, 165-66, 169-70, 176, 185, 191-3, 195, 210, 213, 229, 244, 256, 265, 343, 344, 352
Bridging Techniques, 134, 228

C

Candace Pert, 16
Carl Jung, 6, 11, 198, 202
Catherine Ponder, 279, 282
Causal Event, 19, 93, 94, 100, 105, 109, 121, 124, 129, 134, 135, 138, 143, 147. 165, 166, 182, 191, 207, 240, 244, 265, 321, 349, 349, 353
Central Nervous System, 12
Chair Therapy, 344, 198
Charles Poyen, 10
Charles Tebbetts, 200, 351
Child, 16, 17, 19, 30, 31, 36, 43, 44, 56, 57, 63, 64, 67, 68. 96-98. 113, 114, 125, 131, 136, 141,

Re-Parenting, 15, 16, 29, 31, 57, 62, 97, 131, 153, 154, 199, 200, 204, 205, 211, 212, 214, 215, 220, 222, 229, 252, 260, 262, 267, 268, 273, 276, 291, 292, 295, 303, 304, 321, 351, 353
Resistance, 6, 7, 52, 65, 72-74, 80, 82, 102, 105, 115, 126, 128, 152, 155, 162, 167, 229
Re-Story, 131, 213, 222, 321, 322
Reticular Activating System, 43
Robert Scaer, 100, 165
Roger Callahan, 101, 347
Roger Fisher, 39
Roy Hunter, 200, 351

S
Sad, 33, 65, 68, 69, 92, 94, 95, 113, 114, 123, 127, 145, 150, 151, 159, 168, 169, 173, 187, 188, 190, 191, 201, 215, 282, 283, 288, 301, 302
Seal, 64, 66, 71, 80, 81, 88, 106, 107, 117. 118, 170, 171, 176, 177. 216, 217, 225, 233, 268, 272, 298
Seal Pattern, 170, 171, 176, 177, 216, 217, 223
Secondary Gain, 73, 74
Secondary Issues, 138
Seed-Planting Event, 165, 181, 185, 349
Self-Forgiveness, 267, 268, 295, 296

Self-Healing, 3, 15, 74, 120, 126, 128, 129, 202, 221, 246, 256, 291, 317, 320
Sensory Information, 186
Sentence Stems
Completion, 89, 288
Session Map, 191, 192, 195, 228, 239
Set-Up Phase, 27, 36, 89. 129, 228
Sexual, 258
Simpson Protocol, 305
Sleep, 8, 10, 11, 13, 24, 40, 66, 205, 254, 255, 256, 258, 274, 354
Somatic Bridge, 143, 144, 352
Somnambulism, 79, 80, 90, 120, 134, 305, 352, 353, 354
Sore Spot, 112
Spontaneous Regression, 156-160
Stephen Parkhill, 4, 18, 144, 184, 222, 245
Steve Wells, 102
Stir Up the Feeling, 148, 149, 160, 228
Story, 18, 36-39, 66, 81, 93, 120, 124, 131, 152, 161, 165, 169, 172, 179, 180, 191, 192, 195, 213, 220, 222, 229, 233, 237-40, 255, 256, 265, 279, 287, 299, 307, 309-11, 313, 315, 316, 321, 322
Subconscious Solution, 97, 121, 122
Subjective Unit of

Perception, 312, 271
Trauma, 31,44, 71, 100, 101,
124, 125, 153, 165-67, 176, 181,
193, 206, 268, 318, 344, 346,
349
Trigger, 14, 18, 35, 41, 84, 91-
93, 97, 101, 142, 147, 166, 172,
184, 186, 188, 192, 237, 240,
242-244, 251, 253-257, 261-63,
265, 267, 269, 304, 343

U
Ultra-Depth, 305, 353
Ultra-Height, 354
Unconscious, 4, 11, 13, 35, 36,
53, 55, 57, 121, 137, 158, 162,
172, 181, 182, 188, 189, 198,
244, 255, 262, 263, 267, 291,
350, 353
Unconscious Mind, 53, 55, 353
Uncovering, 18, 27, 45, 48, 110,
134, 158, 162, 163-65, 171, 173,
174, 177, 184-86, 191, 195, 197,
208, 216, 219, 220, 228, 229,
288
Unforgiveness, 286

Universal Healing, 18, 27, 80,
90, 91, 102, 106, 107, 117, 233,
265, 275

V
Validation, 81, 85-87, 105, 116,
128, 138, 155, 284
Verification Phase, 191, 230,
231
Virginia Satir, 198, 199, 232, 274

W
Watch and Wait, 145, 156
Watkins, 143, 200, 343
Weight, 13, 16. 40, 46, 89, 99,
122, 189, 226, 246, 247, 253,
255, 257-259, 287, 303
Windows to The Soul, 293
Wisdom Cycle, 313, 315

Y
Youth Cycle, 314, 316

Wendie Webber

With over thirty years of experience as a healing practitioner, Wendie brings a broad range of skills to her unique approach to regression to cause hypnosis.

She is an Omni-Hypnosis graduate, 5-Path practitioner, Transactional hypnotherapist, Alchemical hypnotherapist, Satir Transformational Systemic therapist, and Regression Hypnotherapy Boot Camp participant.

Before hypnosis, Wendie owned a self-help bookstore where she explored spirituality, psychology, and energy-based healing.

Wendie is the recipient of the 2006 5-PATH Leadership Award and the 2019 Gerald F. Kein OMNI Award for Excellence in Hypnotism.

She enjoys an eclectic lifestyle on Vancouver Island, British Columbia, Canada, surrounded by nature, oracles, and cats. Her courses are available at Tribeofhealers.com